WEAR THE DAMN SWIMSUIT

Lessons and Stories From Cancer and Life

BY ASHLI BREHM

FOREWORD BY PAMELA BUFFETT

Cover layout by Kelsey Scofield.

Typesetting by Kelly Creative. www.kelleycreative.design

CONTENTS

FOREWORD

At many moments in my life, angels of love have appeared. Among those angels is Ashli Brehm, the author who penned the book you are holding in your hands. Ashli's words have touched my heart in a way that is unimaginable.

Having experienced my own sadness and loss in life, Ashli's words deeply resonated with me. I related to the way that she wrote about experiencing joy, even through pain. I decided I wanted to know her in person. I felt she was someone with whom I wanted to talk about the way that sorrow seems to go hand-in-hand with gratitude.

Ashli's stories and lessons in this book are profound. She is a woman who, I believe, writes what many of us have experienced. She is courageous and compassionate. She is authentic and empathetic. She is strong and her words have the ability to make you feel stronger as you read them. She is a bright light of hope.

Ashli's words give meaning to one's internal thoughts. Her willingness to share, even the very sad and difficult parts of her life, so that others might find comfort and hope, is truly magical. Her words are a beautiful illustration of how it takes a team of earthly angels to lift us through our pain.

Many people are like Ashli, and have endured hardships in life. People – whether rich or poor, old or young, male or female – encounter loss. Each one of us experiences pain. In reading these lessons, I believe that we are reminded that we are all surviving something. It is the process of survival that, though it doesn't erase the sadness, makes life a true journey.

As you read this book about the lessons Ashli has learned through cancer and life, I hope you experience her beautiful heart, her light, and her humble spirit.

Wishing you much love, gratitude, and healing as you experience your own path. I hope that you find your very own ways to *Wear The Swimsuit* in your life.

Pamela Buffett

To the people who raised me, the people I'm raising, and the man I get to raise people with, I thank God for each of you every day.

LESSON:

Wear the Damn Swimsuit

*P*eople often ask, "What did you learn from having cancer?"

Oooooey boy.

How could I possibly produce a high-level-bulleted-review of the things I learned through this life-changing event?

How do I explain how it felt to look at my 6, 4, and 2-year-old and feel like I had somehow derailed their ability to *just be* kids for their childhoods? How do I explain what it felt like to look at my husband and think that I completely screwed him out of the woman he had thought he'd married? How do I explain what I learned from putting my life in the hands of doctors, nurses, God, family, and friends? How do I possibly tell another human how I now look at the world so incredibly differently through my cancer-spectacles? How do I sum it up?

WELP. Here goes:

Wear the damn swimsuit.

Yes. Wear the **DAMN** swimsuit. With a big ol' emphasis on the damn. Because, along with wearing the swimsuit, I decided through cancer and life that swearing is necessary when it's necessary.

The swimsuit. *Why* the *swimsuit?*

Well. If you had asked me at age 5, "Ashli, name something you will use to mark time in your years on this earth," never would I ever have thought that it would be a *swimsuit.*

Even if you live in Northern California or Austin, Texas, where the sun shines almost all year and snow rarely—if ever—falls, there are seasons. Of weather. And of life. For me, a Nebraska born and raised gal, once summer came to an end, so did my daily use of my swimsuit. By the time it was the season for sunning and pool-ing again, a year had passed and growth and time necessitated purchasing a new swimsuit.

So the swimsuit. One-part lycra-swimgarb. One-part marker-of-time.

My mom has often replayed to me the tale of the day that, with all my 3-year-old moxie, I disappeared from the deck of the local pool, only to return sans swimsuit. Naked as a newborn babe. In only my skin and my smile, I scaled the ladder to the high dive and plunged right into the water below. Apparently, my short three years of life up to that point had not yet instilled in me the fear that one is *supposed* to have of death by drowning. Or the terror that I eventually developed of showing off my physical form.

The swimsuit. When I was 7 or 8, I stood in a department store dressing room and looking over my shoulder, peering into the mirror, I checked out my bottom. It was adorned with ruffles, something that one can pull off as simply darling at 7 or 8. I liked everything about the two-piece-black-and-white-polka-dotted number. I stuck out my belly, making it round as could be. I was in love with the freedom of my belly button. The only emotion accompanying the try-on-session was joy over another summer, soon to be spent as a fish.

2

The swimsuit. When I was 13, I got my first *real* bikini. The kind with a clasp in the back and underwire on the front. It was blue and white gingham with a yellow daisy in the middle. The amount of padding almost made me look like I had a little more in my bust than just nipples on top of skin. I can still recall feeling so excited that day to take that suit out for its inaugural spin.

But then I walked around the pool deck with my friends and flung my towel out in front of me in the spot we'd claimed for sunning. I watched my friends do the same, mesmerized by what they were wearing. It was my first memory of taking stock of their suits. I was 13, and, sizing up my body next to theirs, I learned the *feeling* of inadequacy. And I felt fear. It was my first memory of a swimsuit producing fear. The first memory where boobs, or lack thereof, produced a negative feeling in me.

The swimsuit. When I was 17, I wore a red lifeguard suit. My uniform. It was a means to making a paycheck while getting to hang out with my friends. Daily, I compared my thighs and lack of abs, and I wished that I had a different body to don the suit. I had begged for some curves in the years following the daisy-adorned suit, and when they arrived, settling on my thighs and my waist, I wanted to return the items to sender. This was not what I'd envisioned when I put in my order for *curves*. My relationship and infatuation with *the swimsuit* had drastically changed since the days of the ruffle-bottomed two-piece.

The swimsuit. In the years that followed high school, I mostly avoided wearing a swimsuit. I can recall a time in my sophomore year of college when I was invited for a swim at a hotel pool with my now-husband and his family. I sat in a chair, outside the pool, fully clothed. I felt better suited in something that covered any and all curves that my skin had formed around.

I know it is often said that you can't really love someone until you decide to love yourself. But it was through being loved by the man I met in college that I started to feel comfortable with myself again.

The swimsuit. When I was 23, I went on my honeymoon in paradise. It was a turning point from my youth to my growth. And tucked in my bag were swimsuits. One was a white eyelet bikini. I lazed by the pool by day, drank dirty martinis by night, ate dessert after every meal. Together, my new husband and I soaked up every second of magic.

But it was in pregnancy that I felt *it*. The emotion of beauty. How the stuff that shines from the inside out becomes a vibe that you possess. How something can feel like every bit of goodness. It felt like I was a true conduit to a miracle. It didn't matter what I was wearing or how I looked. When I could place my hand on a firm, round belly, it felt like if anything in life could be beauty-full—that was it.

The babies were on and off and on and off and on and off. Four pregnancies. Three babies. A span of years. My body, a far cry from the ruffle-bottomed-bikini girl. As bodies do with time and age and babies, things became more marked up from the making of it all. Over and over. And over and over.

As I look down the road I've taken to travel to my current place, I can see how my skin has held to me with everything it has. It has become and unbecome day after day with me. I have encountered so many different reflections of my form, bouncing back from a plate of glass. I know that I have allowed my heart to be influenced by the size of my pants and the number on a scale. I've let my opinion of who I am be influenced by everything from the length of my toes to the curvature of my butt.

Through all my shapes and sizes, wins and losses, highs and lows, ebbs and flows, I can hear a tinge of regret as my mind that whispers: *Ashli, there are a bajillion and ten different things people fear in this world and you feared a swimsuit.*

An outfit. A stitching together of fabrics. A physical item designed as a means to get into a swimming pool, walk in the sand, or run into crashing waves. An outfit that can be worn to move your muscles and be active.

The swimsuit.

In the last few years, I've experienced the reality that someday I won't have this body of mine anymore. My body has been torn all apart and put back together. And while I know so many say they have no regrets, as I reflect on my years so far, I can't help but ask myself... ***what did I miss because I wouldn't wear the swimsuit?***

What did I miss because at times I had more anxiety over the thought of wearing a suit than I did when I rode in a plane and skydived down over the blue ocean? Because I let my outer container be the boss of my inner self?

What did I miss?

Even if you *no-regrets-people* would say I didn't truly *miss* anything because where I am today is exactly where I'm meant to be, I still wonder: *how will I make sure I wear the swimsuit moving forward?* How will I constantly remember that I *get* to live? That I must truly be alive for these years I call life?

Well, first...I gotta let the past go. Yep. I've reached my Elsa-on-top-of-the-ice-mountain moment and I'm telling myself to *let it go*. Letting go is very different than forgetting. I don't have to forget the past. In fact, I don't want to. But if I want to wear the swimsuit, I've got to pull up my socks and move forward.

I've got to remind myself each and every day that I *get* to wake up. That I *get* to be *here.* And that I *get* the chance to wear the damn swimsuit, every day. Because the swimsuit? It's a metaphor for all the things we've allowed to hold us back. The fears we've let freeze us.

So I must tell you. What I learned from cancer is that I need to wear the damn swimsuit.

Now. Perhaps you've arrived here and are thinking, *This gal is bizarro. Who would ever be afraid of a swimsuit?* Fair enough. We all have different fears and challenges. Heck, maybe you rock the swimsuit every stinkin' chance you get.

But have you ever backed away from something because you feared you were less capable or cool or talented? Have you ever sat out an adventure because you were worried about what other people would think of you? Have you allowed insecurities or a lack of confidence to keep you from doing something you really wanted to do? *That's* your swimsuit.

Unless you can push yourself past it, you're never going to allow your spirit and spark to fully unfurl into this universe.

Cancer taught me that life and doing and being feels more life-full when I step into the suit and get my booty off the edge of the pool. And maybe even closing my eyes and getting deep into the water. Doing the things that life and humanness have conditioned our minds to be afraid of. Do—as the young kids are sayin'—all the things.

And don't *just* wear the damn swimsuit.

Eat the donut. Yes. Maybe you're fearing the donut or you've labeled it as "bad." It's time to let that feeling go. So go ahead and eat one every so often.

Dance when there's no dance floor. Only you possess your sweet dance moves.

Sing out loud like you're vying for a spinny chair to turn your way. Sing. In the shower. In your car. On the stage.

Take an evening jog when the sun is just starting to set and the chill of the night is mixing with the warmth of the day. Smell the dust that rises up when the sun connects with the horizon. Take a deep breath as the present day melts into the past.

Tell someone *thank you*. Call someone and say...*thank you*. Call your dad. Call your Aunt Deb. Call one of the million Jamie's or Jennis you knew high school (Or maybe the Shanda). Call the teacher who, even 22 years later, you still quote. Or the one who didn't even know they would forever live in a little spot in your heart because they introduced you to books like, *The Last of the Really Great Whangdoodles*. Call a person who you are grateful for. Tell them that they have made a difference in your life.

Snuggle just a little longer with your toddler. Or your cat. Or your favorite book. Let your dishes wait. Snuggling with dishes isn't even comfortable. And there will *always* be dishes.

Write. Share. Tell your story. You're the only you there is, and that is generally interesting to other people.

Travel and see the world—or even just the neighboring town— through your eyes. Expand your understanding of how living somewhere else forms different beliefs, languages, and hearts. Grow your view. Grow your heart.

Figure out where you came from. Lift up your family tree and examine your roots. Learn what those who came before did to make sure you could be here. Go out on a limb. Follow your branches. Know that there is so much more *out there* beyond you.

Ask for your grandma's banana bread recipe. Cook alongside your mom. Learn to cook your favorite food. Or find the place where you like it best. And then eat that food. Carbs will likely not kill you. Eat fresh foods when they're available. Eat local foods where they are tabled. And gosh freaking darn it, if you like dessert, eat it. Death by chocolate is far less common than most other causes of death.

Read the words you love voraciously. Educate your mind. Open your world. Never feel guilty for not getting the laundry done because you were reading. There will always be more laundry.

Watch your favorite flicks from your childhood. If they're screening at your local theater, buy a ticket and prepare to feel like you're 9 again.

Lie in the grass and let your dog rest with you. Look up. At the clouds. At the wide-open sky. At heaven. At the world that covers you. Soak up all that is bigger than you will ever ever become. Revel in being small and feel gratitude for everything that goes right in the great expanse of the universe, every single day.

Spend time with people who make you laugh. Cry. *Feel*. Ask them questions. *Actually* listen to the answers. Get to really know those around you. Let them know you. These are your people.

Pray for the person whose hand you hold during Worship. Send strength to someone you don't even know. Put out positive vibes. Spread love and light. However it is that you can transfer your thoughts to someone, try and do that.

Do a cannonball into the cold pool. And if you don't want to worry about the swimsuit, then drop it like it's hot and skinny dip.

Milk a goat. For real, try it out. Touch a snake, even if you need to close your eyes. Catch lightning bugs in a jar. See, feel, and experience all the creatures sharing this world with you.

Skip a rock down the road as you walk. Stick your bare feet in the water along a creek. Take opportunities to feel natural in nature.

Put a plant on your desk. Paint a wall with a huge mural. Frame pictures and moments that make you smile. Or at least find one that you are claiming a little as *yours*.

Try a totally new thing. Make your own microwave popcorn instead of buying the packaged kind. Learn the guitar. Jump from a plane. Do something out of the ordinary.

Go golfing. Take up tap dancing. Water ski. Register for a 5k. Do something to surprise your body and your muscles and your agility. Stretch yourself.

Sweat. From running. From biking. From dancing. From laughing. Feel the satisfaction and release that comes from being active.

Kiss. Hug. Hold a hand. Have a cup of coffee across from someone who makes you think. Feel what closeness brings. Connect to other humans.

Love without hesitation. Out of all the things in this world that are subject to limitations, love is not one of them. It is not a finite resource. Give of it generously.

Shine your own light and inevitably you will cut through the darkness.

When something comes along that you want to do but fear is holding you back, get off the pool deck and make a splash.

Live the day. Whatever living feels like for *you*. Live the day that is happening right now.

Life is shorter than short, no matter how long yours gets to be.

Wear the damn swimsuit.

LESSON:

I'm Kind of a Long Story

Hi, there. I'm Ashli. Ashli Brehm. Let's just clear something up right off the bat. I know that the chance that you just read my last name and thought it is pronounced Bremm is pretty high. But really, it's Brame. I know it seems like a tomato-tomahto thing, but in order for you to really know me, I feel I should tell you how to pronounce my name. And I know I made a big ta-do already about life being short and now I'm telling you that I'm kind of a long story. Just go with it, cool?

I was born in a small town. If you don't now find yourself singing John Cougar Mellencamp lyrics, then maybe this book isn't for you. I grew up in Wilber, Nebraska (yes, Wilber, *the best small town ever*. Not the pig). I was the third born child of my father, Tad, who listens like no one I've ever met, and my mother, Dodie, who comforts people just by inviting them into our home for a meal. (Before we go any further, *yes*, those are the names of my parents. Tad. And Dodie. And, yes, they somehow managed to find one another.)

I grew up in the '80s and '90s in a blue 1970's ranch. On 6th street. Didja get that? I shared a room with my sister and built-in best friend, Danielle. We could often be found dancing to the Beaches' soundtrack, playing Barbies, or watching TGIF, depending on the day. My brother, Matthew, the lone boy to two sisters, often had a friend around, and spent most of his time shooting baskets past sunset. We had a miniature schnauzer, Molly. And for one school year, we hosted a foreign exchange student, Tjaaktje.

I had, what I consider to be, a solid foundation. A good childhood. A happy upbringing.

I graduated high school in a class of 40ish people. I attended college. Joined a sorority (Holla to all my Phi Mu sisters). Met Adam Brehm. Got married. Lived in Austin for a hot minute. Moved back to Nebraska. And boom. That's the highlight reel.

In 2008, I began recording my life on a blog—more specifically *my* blog—Baby on the Brehm. Born out of my desire to chronicle my pregnancy with my firstborn, Barrett, Baby on the Brehm began as a central brain-dump of my thoughts as a twenty-something woman embarking on the wild world of having humans.

I wrote about Adam, my husband, prepping the nursery. About the high-risk nature of our pregnancy. And when Barrett arrived a month early, I shared about being a stay-at-home mom to an under-5-pound peanut who screamed all day and partied all night. I wrote about how I couldn't fully wrap my mind around how it felt as though I'd known this little nugget my whole life, but yet also seemed to know nothing about him at all.

I wrote through missing the identity I'd had in my career. The job that I'd done as a non-profit development director, raising funds for cystic fibrosis, had become the majority of my life. I missed my coworkers and my volunteers. I missed my boss, Shannon, and all of her words of wisdom. I missed dressing up every day and leaving my house. I missed social interaction. And as I sunk into motherhood, I found myself smelling only of breast milk and Oreos. And wondering if I was, or ever would be, a good mom.

I wrote through the bliss of welcoming a second son into our family, Jonah. Born at 36 weeks, also under 5 pounds. Making the choice to stay home with two boys under three. And then, eventually, going back to work.

I wrote through a lost pregnancy. And the loss of a part of myself in that process.

I wrote about our joy of having a third boy.

Yes. Three boys. I know you might be asking yourself, *I wonder if she'll try for a girl.* Um, no. We tried for humans, we got them. And while three boys make for a constant stream of pee on the bathroom wall, I'm content with my brood of brothers.

I shared through a third high-risk pregnancy. We're sort of *same song different verse* folks around here. A third premature delivery; this one at 32 weeks. Harrison tipped the scales at 3 pounds even. And I captured the first 6 weeks of his life that were spent in the NICU.

I wrote about my husband. My marriage. My family. My friendships. Motherhood. I had written so many posts and started to feel as though my next writing project should be a book on Motherhood.

Then came a dramatic subplot. The storyline took an unforeseen turn when, at age 33, I was diagnosed with breast cancer. My boys, the primary subjects of my blog posts up until then, were 6, 4, and 2. I contemplated shutting down Baby on the Brehm and fighting breast cancer privately.

But writing had been my release. It offered a catharsis that had become therapeutic. And cancer was definitely going to take every kind of therapy I could get.

So it continued. The writing. The sharing. The real feelings of my real life. Through cancer, I chronicled it all.

Through writing and prayer and love and chemotherapy, I found healing. And I found myself in awe of all of the ways life was happening *at* me. All the ways that even in alllllll the pain, there seemed to be a purpose to my getting to *be*.

I started writing a book again and again. I would find myself worried about how someone might take *this* or feel about *that*. I would mull over my writing style or my made-up words, wondering if they'd make sense to anyone else. And then I realized that I needed to just be me. And that is when I started writing *this* book.

As you read, you might find yourself saying, "Well, I don't agree with that." You may find yourself thinking, *why did she have to use the word fuck? Is that just to be edgy? Why is this girl talking about Jesus? This was not advertised as a Christian book. Why is she writing about medical stuff when she's not a doctor or about sex when she's a mother? Why is she acting like she was gonna die when she got to escape the grips of cancer? How can she think life is so bright when the world is filled with so much darkness?*

I wrote this book as me. As me as me gets. It is written in the form of separate essays and chunks, each written independently from the other and then woven together, all with at least a thread of goodness.

———

This book is a collection of words and lessons that *I* took with me from cancer and life. Some have made me sad. Some have made me laugh. Some have caused me to shout profanity. Some have made me feel free. The lessons and stories are realizations that have changed the way I look at my husband, love my people, view social media, and make the choice to get out of bed in the morning. Lessons that I wanted to capture for my boys. Words that I wanted to be here if, for some reason, I am not. And, FWIW (how the young whipper snappers say *for what it's worth*) my beautiful boys – Barrett, Jonah, and Harrison – currently refer to the book as *Wear the D Swimsuit* because they are aware that some parts of it are acceptable for them to consume today and some are meant for them to read later.

There are lessons that I likely met prior to cancer, but they became clearer through different challenges and glimmers of goodness. Some that I didn't expect I'd learn in my thirties. Some that I didn't ever think I would have to learn. Some of these lessons came in big-bright-beacons, shining down in a moment of total despair. Some came through the cracks that let the light shine through. Others came in the feeling and healing of one of the hardest times I've endured as a human.

The lessons are yours to noodle on. There are stories that *I* hope give *you* hope. I hope they will help you feel like you are doing the best you can, and know that the truth is, we are all surviving something.

You may not have had cancer. You may not even have breasts. But, in being human, we all have a life, and I believe these lessons to be mostly universal for people who get to spend any amount of time here.

I'm Ashli (sometimes known as Baby on the Brehm) and for my *short* 37-years on this earth, I feel like mine has already become kind of a *long* story.

Honestly though?

I sure do prefer that to the alternative.

LESSON:

There Is Goodness Here

I sat on a boat. I'd just gotten off a thrilling ride on a Big Mabel, a large bench-ish tube that's towed behind a boat. The Mabel's bouncing had necessitated some mad Kegel action so as not to pee all over myself. Because, well, ever since birthing babies, *The Great Breast Cancer Invasion* in my 33rd year, and going through menopause at 34, my 35-year-old lady parts were not quite as spry as they once were.

I sat on the boat as we sped around the lake. I was in a one-piece swim dress. A *swim dress*. Because I'm apparently at an age where sometimes, a swimsuit looks a little more like a dress than a bikini. This particular swim dress had become my freedom cry.

It was the same swimwear that had inspired me at the beginning of the summer to go down to the edge of the dock, wave my hands in the air, and celebrate **wearing the damn swimsuit.** It was that day that I wrote a blog post that went, what is known in the internet world as, *viral.* I find *viral* to be a very odd word to describe something that you *want* but that is the word, for real. I wore the swimsuit that day, after having gone through a personal shitstorm, thrilled to be alive. And I wrote about wearing the swimsuit in life.

And now the summer was drawing to a close and I sat on the boat that day in a state of contentment. Feeling at ease. Feeling lucky. Feeling, as I looked around and took in the situation, that I'd somehow gotten *it all*.

Yes. *All*. My happily ever after.

I felt the *goodness*.

The goodness of getting to listen to one of my three blondies, giggling all over himself. The goodness of watching Adam—my husband/best guy I know/the love of my life—relaxed and savoring the sunshine.

The goodness in seeing Barrett, our *Oldest* and wise-beyond-his-8-years, hanging in the sunshine at the *helm*. Watching him forget for a moment that he so often wants to grow up. Watching him just be 8. Satisfied and needing nothing more than that day.

The goodness of seeing Jonah—the middle man, the middle child, the *Middlest*—sit next to Adam, laughing and poking at his belly. I watched him giggle all over himself and hoped he'd always have such a capacity for joy.

The glow and shine of goodness as I looked down at my thigh and viewed a blonde, curly-mopped 3-year-old, Harrison, the baby of the brothers, the *Littlest*, sacked out and sprawled on the boat bench...long eyelashes resting atop his cheek.

Maybe it was the sun or the water. Perhaps it was the right cocktail of chemistry -- an anti-anxiety medication -- mixed with my biology. Maybe it was the sheer grace of God. But this little moment where everything in my world all felt in its right place was so *big* to me.

I knew my life was a lot messier than I ever thought it would be. My mess of cancer staking claim on my right boob when I was 33. Somehow though, it felt like a *beautiful* mess. The magic of that day felt worth the mess and the hardships if even to just get to that *very* moment.

I seem delusional, right? All this talk of magic and goodness makes me sound like some sort of '70s Flower Child who just ingested magic mushrooms or is wandering through the desert, high on peyote. Because there's no way that being on a boat with three kids can be *that* relaxing. Or *that* magical. Surely one of them needed to poop at an inconvenient time or another screamed because he didn't get the seat next to grandma.

I assure you, I was not under the influence of anything outside of sunshine and survival.

Life was filled with goodness that day.
It had been filled with goodness before that day.
And it's been filled with goodness since.

Life had also been hard.
Painful.
Scary.

But it's a beautiful thing when, in dealing with the hard, you are also shown the goodness.

Books upon books have already established: Life includes hard.

A day can be hard.
A week.
A season.
An existence.

BUT.

In our biggest moments of loss, sorrow, and pain, fires seemingly burn us to the ground, ending the life we knew. That part sucks. It is complete shit. But then, sometimes, smoke drifts up from the ashes. And in that rising is the beginning of something new. *That* is the *goodness.*

I have never been a natural Pollyanna and I don't know that optimism always came naturally to me. I was always much more of a realist. Because life doesn't always feel magical or good or easy, does it?

Every single one of us have had hard days. We all have things that suck and days that are shit and periods of life where we feel like we're flailing. If you were to make a *list o' hard stuff* it would be replete with adversity and trials.

Yet, there's something wild about the hard stuff being all listed out. The list would not be your *life*. It would not tell your whole story.

That list would *only* be the hard. It wouldn't contain the sprinkles and sparks and infusion of *goodness* that comes with the hard.

On a particularly crap day when we are exhausted, worn, and all used up, it can be hard to catch the glimmers. So. In my post-cancer life, if the day has been particularly challenging or difficult, I try to take a moment to write it out. It could be on a note in my phone. Or the back of a receipt as I sit in the carpool lane. Or if I'm totally stuck, drained, or depleted, I may do a *fast five* list in my head as I lay my head on the pillow.

My list of glimmers in the darkest days come from the backdrop of my story:

...from being born into a safe home with loving parents who inspired me to dream
...to growing up with siblings who I respect, admire, and actually like
...from learning about community in my hometown
...to the friends and family and framily who are goodness personified
...from the college experience that helped me grow in knowledge and confidence and make friends who are now an extension of me
...to allowing me to meet the very mate for which my soul was shaped

...from gaining another family who are described as in-laws even though that feels so insufficient

... to my work life with mentors who never stopped believing in me

...from a squad who never stops showing up

...to my doctors who were there every minute I needed them in order to survive and who continue to be there every moment I thrive

...from a pastor, church, and Creator who know my mustard seed and water it endlessly

...to getting to watch a sunset, drink a warm cup of coffee, listen to Josh Radin and Nora Jones tunes as my kids circle around me in a complete flurry of motion

...from all the littlest morsels that take me through waking up and putting my feet on the floor for another day

...to getting to rest my head in a nook of calm at the end of each day

My goodness can come from all of those larger themes.

Or sometimes the list comes in a moment of a particular day:

...drinking coffee alone in the dark of the morning
...playing air hockey with my boys
...a hamburger from *Block 16*
...a margarita with my sister-in-law
...doing yoga next to a friend
...reading puns from my dad
...my mom giving me the weather forecast
...a ten-minute walk around the block
...my brother sending a funny tweet
...messages about nipples from FUBC (FU Breast Cancer) gals
...a random driveway chat with my neighbor
...a phone call with my sister
...drinking an old-fashioned with my hubs
...the boys not mauling each other in the insanity of bedtime
...a dance in the kitchen with my main squeeze
...a clean kitchen counter
...Marco Polo videos my Polo Peeps
...showering *and* fixing my hair

Those little bits feel like a million little reminders that while the hard is *hard*, the good is also *so* good.

It doesn't make the hard stuff disappear. But those things do, for me, seem to make it *worth* it all.

Sometimes I just need to acknowledge the existence of goodness and collect it all up in a memory jar that I can take out when life loses its luster.

So let those little lights shine in when you can. The little bits of goodness can brighten the dark. Not because life and the world are full of so much bad... but because it can all be so good.

There is goodness here. Oh, what a gorgeous gift that is.

LESSON:

It's My Life and I'll Cry If I Want to

*I*t was a Monday morning.

It must be noted that the day prior was Sunday. And while I remember very little about that Sunday, I know it was a Sunday because as I learned at Blue Door Preschool when I was 4-years-old, Monday, without fail, follows Sunday.

I wish I could remember more about that Sunday. I know that we went to church because I blogged about it the next day. I know that our house was in disarray as we'd recently moved from our first family home to a new-to-us house. I know that I'd been frazzled over the last six weeks while we sold our first home and slowly moved all our belongings over to the new backdrop of our story. But I wish I could remember more about that Sunday.

I wish I could remember what it had felt like to feel *in control* of my life. I wish I could remember what the sunshine looked like, or even if it had been sunny that Sunday. I wish I could remember what it felt like to lay my head down that night, my three boys, Barrett, Jonah, and Harrison, tucked in their beds and crib, my body tucked beside Adam's.

But I don't remember that normal Sunday. So often, we don't store those normal days in our memory database. The major storage is utilized for the big moments or the things that change us and form us.

That Monday in late August, I was getting my three boys ready for school and pre-school. I threw on Athleta exercise capris, a hot pink scoop-neck shirt from Old Navy, and a Target Sports Bra designed with hot pink, white, and black diamonds and zig-zags.

My boys were 6, 4, and 2. I'd recently gotten into a groove of exercising each day. The exercising was something that, for the six-months leading up to that Monday, I'd made a priority amongst the demands of being a little people logistics manager. My days were made up of drop-offs, pick-ups, naptimes, and snacks.

I filed through my day as I pulled the sports bra over my head. And then, in the same fashion that I'd done morning after morning over the last six months, I cupped my left boob and positioned it in the sports bra. Then the right. Wearing a sports bra post-babies took some *finesse, wrangling, and groping* to get my itty-bitty boobies *just so* and in place.

And there it was. On the right side, there was *a something*.

A lump.

I touched it again. I cupped it. Poked at it. Massaged it. I really should have introduced myself before I got so up in its grill. There was definitely *a thing*. This *something* inside my sports bra. This *something* inside my breast on the outer right underside. I felt it again and again.

It felt hard-ish.

Movable.

When did that arrive? I wondered. I didn't know. I'd weaned my third-born from my carton's five months prior and watched them drain down into deflated size A's that required very little maintenance outside of the sports bra placement. Heck. As a mom of three boys under 6, I couldn't even keep track of which meal offering one of them had scoffed at two nights prior. Or which day I'd last washed my hair. Or which season of Real Housewives was currently happening. There was little to no chance of me having kept track of something that was attached to me day in and day out.

So I did what any mom in the 21st century does. I texted a few of my girlfriends, a few of my besties, who had also nursed and then weaned.

"Did anyone have anything hard left over after nursing?"

Two nos. One yes.

Okay. *This is just some milk duct situation,* I thought. Some little duct in there must have gotten clogged up, the milk has turned to cottage cheese and I need to empty that sucker of its curds and whey.

My boobs. While my husband stated over and over that he was a big fan, I saw them to be in a dismal state. They sorta looked like marbles had been dropped into deflated balloons. And the nipples appeared as though to be barely hanging on. I had nursed all three boys for over a year and my boys had drained my drinkers dry. Into Tiny. Little. Molehills. Surely there was no reason to make a mountain out of them.

But that *something*...the small something accompanying my small set...it didn't feel like nothing.

That Monday, after the dust kicked up by the morning chaos had settled, I phoned the office of my general practitioner, Dr. Saxena (aka Dr. S). I explained that it was time for a blood pressure check-in and *ohandalsobytheway* perhaps she could assess the *something* on my chest.

I was on the books for *Friday.*

Tuesday morning, I woke up anxious. By Wednesday, I was stewing.

I obsessed over the lump. I think my breasts got more action in that week than they got in all my years as a teenager. I felt the area, again and again, certain that it was growing by the hour. By Wednesday night, I lay in bed next to my husband, feeling it and trying to determine if it felt different or seemed to disappear as I was horizontal. It didn't. I cried. I shared with Adam that I was feeling excessively anxious about the visitor. I told him I desperately wished I could go into the doctor the next day so she could tell me I was crazy and I could get back to my regularly scheduled life of worrying about whether my kid practiced his spelling words or not. Adam hugged me, listened to me, and true to his role in our relationship, tried to quell my fears. Having known me for over a decade, he knew that I was prone to worry. And that in all likelihood, I'd just have to get through the doctor's appointment to get over my fears.

By Friday, I was a fucking maniac. You might not like swearing but I want to go ahead and lay this on you: I use colorful language. I wasn't just flipping or freaking scared. I wasn't forking or effing. I was fucking crazed in the head over this lump.

I needed a person who knew about such things to tell me that this *something* was *nothing*.

My two youngest boys, Jonah and Harrison, came with me to my doctor's office.

It was September 4th.

The beginning of one of my favorite months of the year.

The near-ending of our summer. The near beginning of our Fall.

And, what I realize now, was also the beginning of my own fall.

I changed into a hospital gown. It was soft and white with a faint bluish design. I tied it around me and looked at my bare legs that were splotched with a bluish hue and covered in goose bumps. I folded my pants and set them on a chair with my other clothes. I stepped up and placed myself on the exam table. The boys took turns sitting up with me, crinkling the paper beneath us and asking me why I wasn't wearing my clothes.

Dr. S entered the room. She said hi to the boys. They chattered back. We made some small talk and discussed my blood pressure. The boys busied themselves as we talked. Looking down at my chart and then looking back at me, Dr. S said, "So you have a lump?"

"Yeah. I just noticed it on Monday. I'm not sure if it's *something* left from nursing..." I trailed off, trying to keep control over my emotions.

She asked me to lay back and raise my arms up over my head. She felt both breasts in what seemed to be a clinical pattern. With the pads of her fingers mapping out my breast, she felt the mass that I had first felt on Monday. I saw her look at the ceiling as she felt around it as if to understand the shape in her mind rather than just judging a book by its cover.

"We're going to get a mammogram," she stated matter-of-factly.

"Oh..."

"That way, I'll know exactly what it is. It could be a cyst. But I can't aspirate a cyst unless I know it's actually that. It could be an infection. Inflammation. I just want to get a look at it and get a baseline."

My stomach wanted to throw up all over me. I looked at my two boys' little faces. I wanted to cry. And so, I did. I began with a few warm tears running down my face. My cheeks were flushed. I could feel the warmth spreading. Then more came. Several more. A pool of tears. A runny nose. My cheeks flushed. I didn't feel right. I felt scared. To death.

"Ashli, why are you crying?" Dr. S asked. "It could be many things. We just need to check it out. It could be nothing. I need you to not worry."

Why was I crying?! She simply told me I needed to go get my boobs smooshed. She hadn't said, "By my assessment, this feels like cancer." She had confidently stated that in getting a look at what it was, we would know what it wasn't.

I sat on the exam table, in tears because hearing the words, "We're going to get a mammogram," furthered my fear that this *could* very well be *something*. Every bit of my world seemed to be spinning around me at that moment and I felt like I was Dorothy wrapped up in the tornado and I just wanted to click my freaking heels together and go home. Go back. Back to before that Monday.

My doctor, this woman who had always been so clinical, hugged me as I cried into her white coat.

Dr. S scheduled a mammogram for later that afternoon. The boys and I left the office. I cried as we walked down the hall. As we walked down the stairs. As I looked at the back of their heads bobbing in front of me.

I know what you're thinking at this point in this little story. You are reading this and saying, "Crimenantly, Ashli, *Baby on the Brehm girl*. Get it together. It's *just* a mammogram. Do some yoga. Read your bible. Take a Xanax. Download the Calm app." At least that's what *I* think to myself every time I relive the fact that I cried upon hearing the word *mammogram.*

I started making phone calls.
I called my husband.

"Hey..." I said through an unsteady quiver.
"Hey, what's up?"
"Did I pull you out of a meeting?"
"Yeah... what's going on?"
"I need you to come home. I can't be alone." The floodgates opened. "I have to go in for a mammogram."

We talked logistics. We assumed our usual roles, me the worrier, him the warrior. I cried and gasped. He assured me it was all going to be fine.

In that moment, I was thankful for him always being the yin to my yang in the anxiety department. He could see a playground. I saw 342 ways my child could end up in the ER. He saw a baby-pool for fun in the sun. I saw a child attempting to dive and break their neck or another not knowing how to flip around. He saw a cup as half-full. I saw it as neither full nor empty. Just half. I was, as I liked to refer to myself, *a realist* (although I am sure he would have another word for it...like insane, overbearing, pessimistic, or just plain nutty mcnuttertons). The eternal optimist, he told me that he believed it was *nothing* but he would most definitely head home to help me through this day.

I called my mom in hysterics. Because no matter what age I am or how many kids I have, I am a girl who always needs her mom. My mom, who had worked for an oncologist for 30+ years, assured me that this happens. That women have lumps all the time. They have dense breast tissue. Or cysts. Or a lost Lego floating around in there. Okay, not really a lost Lego, but just the same, she echoed the initial sentiments of, *it could be anything.* In fact, she'd gone through a mammogram and a stereotactic biopsy a few years before, which all ended up being a-ok.

I arrived home. The crying continued. By noon, I had completely jumped the shark from any sort of view of reality and crying was apparently my coping mechanism of choice.

The day took four thousand, twenty-two hours. Okay. It didn't. But the minutes slogged forward as I went through the motions of waiting for the breast-sandwich session.

To pass the time, I cried on my own.
I also cried on Adam.
I cried as I changed into a black dress. Because mammograms should be fancy. Just kidding. It just so happened that the mammogram had wiggled its way onto our Friday calendar of events right between my morning doctor's appointment and the wedding of my sorority Big Sis. A night I'd been looking forward to. But now I stood in a black dress on my Black Friday in tears.

I was still in tears when our babysitter arrived. Libby, a girl who over time and babies had become a part of our family, walked in through the front door and—as had become the trend of the day—I sobbed into her shoulder.

Before we left home I hugged my boys. Not just a hug and a quick peck on the top of their heads, but a *iflcomebackcompletelychangedstillloveme* clinging-to. I even did a grandma-move, cupping their faces to try and memorize every little way that their eyes and noses and lips looked to me that day. I told them each emphatically that I loved them. So much so that, had they been a bit older, they might have thought I was never coming back. And then we left.

We—my husband, myself, my lump, and my little black dress—were on our way to my first ever mammogram. I was silent, holding Adam's hand. Almost holding my breath. Hoping to hold onto the vision of my boys' faces as I got the whole mammogram situation over with.

I was scared.
Really. Horribly. Scared.
As I recounted the number of tears that I'd dished out throughout the week, I felt weak and silly.

I felt embarrassed that I was being so irrational. I felt as though my husband and family were likely planning to commit me until I returned to my normally abnormal self. I felt. And felt. And felt.

While I knew this mammogram was a perfectly reasonable outcome after having a lump checked, I wanted so much to never have gone to the doctor in the first place, to not have set into motion this pendulum that was slowly knocking away my desire for forward momentum.

I knew this was the right thing to do. The responsible action to take as my parents' daughter. My sister and brothers' sibling. The prudent thing as a mother to my boys. I was doing what I would tell anyone else in my position to do. "GO TO THE DOCTOR.

TAKE CARE OF YOUR BODY. IT'S THE ONLY ONE YOU'VE GOT." I was doing the best thing for myself. But this *best thing* also felt like *the worst*.

I prayed (yep. I'm a pray-er). I pleaded in my mind on that car ride, *Dear God. It's Ashli. Please make this nothing.* I knew that if this was nothing, as everyone had tried to reassure me, I was going to feel like a total asshole for all the drama and despair. All the feeling and the frenzy. Yet this was a case where I would be so happy to feel like a total asshole and laugh at myself over and over.

But a little voice whispered in the back of my mind. What if this *was* a *thing*. What if it was cancer. Or a Lego. Well. If the past week was any indication of my inability to cope, I might just need to find me some more Jesus, Lexapro, and/or Tequila if I had any hope of getting through it.

I have it really good, I thought as we parked. I adore my husband. I love my life. I am lucky to be a mom. I really had it good. But I still cried.

I cried that day. So much.
I cried in the weeks that followed. So much.
And I cried when I found out I had cancer.

Because it's my life, and I'll cry if I want to.

LESSON:

I Would Have Died on the Oregon Trail

om! You died of exhaustion," my son cries from the other room.

"Sounds accurate," I answer back.

I guess pioneer moms were not all that different than moms of today, eh?

The Oregon Trail. Did you play that game in your elementary school computer lab? I didn't. It's not because I'm too young to have experienced the hype. I was in elementary school in the late eighties and early '90s, but to my recollection, we did *not* get to experience dying of dysentery.

Thankfully, the toy makers of the aughts have managed to unearth nearly every fad from my childhood and so even if I missed something the first time around, I can catch it on the reunion tour. From Caboodles to scrunchies, my childhood is basically on sale at every big box store for $9.98. And so, of course, I find myself buying memories on occasion.

The Oregon Trail game is back as a sort of board game + card game mash-up that allows players to take a trip back to the days of old and figure out just how successful they would have been as pioneers on the open prairie. I swear, it's not as macabre as it sounds. It's more like Hunger Games meets STEAM (the hot education focus these days that blends science, technology, engineering, the arts, and mathematics) and, as a bonus, might prepare my boys should we ever find ourselves without electricity or water.

They often ask me to play the game and, to be honest, while I am 100% a fan of playing games with the boys and post-cancer me completely believes in saying yes to almost anytime they want to include me, I just can't play it. I already know my own reality. I would have died on the Oregon Trail.

Even when I read it back, it sounds ridiculous. A person can't be so sure that if they'd been alive 100 years ago they would have *expired* quite young. You're calling bullocks on me, I know. But I need you to know about my likely fate on the Oregon Trail in order to really understand my massive breakdown when I was directed to get a mammogram.

I would not have survived the Oregon Trail.

When I was 17-years-old, I went to a doctor who assessed that I had chronic hypertension (the technical term for my ridiculously high blood pressure). The issues with chronic hypertension are many, including a possible stroke, heart damage, or a heart attack.

Luckily, in the year 1999, when I turned 17, there was medicine. Modern medicine.

I know what some of you might be thinking. *I would have just changed my diet. I would have exercised more.* That is wonderful advice and I thank you so much for those ideas. I was, at the time, a three-sport-participant (I'll save the word athlete for the people who have higher ratios of court-to-bench time than I clocked), which kept me pretty active with practice each day of the week. Additionally, during the diagnosis of hypertension, the

31

nurse at the clinic alerted me to the fact that my blood pressure was far too high and I just needed to lose some weight to dial it down. So I did what many teenagers might do should they ever hear the words, "You're just too heavy," and began ridding myself of any food I ingested as fast as possible.

My chronic hypertension was a result of the *genetic lottery*. As such, at 17- years-old, I began seeing a doctor to manage the issue. I remember sitting in the crowded waiting room of his office watching people read the large print Reader's Digest and singing the tune to "one of these things just doesn't belong here" in my head. It occurred to me then that my grandfather's fatal heart attack at 62 and my otherwise healthy parents being on blood pressure medication since I was a child were more likely the culprit for my high pressure than my weight. It occurred to me that even with a bevy of lifestyle changes, this blood pressure situation was probably along for my ride. I was thankful to have a pill to manage my pressures and also keep potential heart damage at bay.

After I was married, I visited a doctor who told me, point blank, "You may want to attempt to start a family soon if you are thinking you are going to have one. With your blood pressure, you could definitely die during childbirth."

Say what?!

Had I flashbacked into Little House on the Prairie? DIE DURING CHILDBIRTH? I was a 24-year-old normal-ish (using that term loosely, of course) person. Yes, I was on blood pressure medication, but surely this man was looking at the wrong chart. Except he wasn't. He elaborated, explaining that while my blood pressure was controlled, oftentimes people with chronic hypertension have a hard time carrying a baby because of placental issues, possible stroke, and, also, stillborn deliveries.

COLOR ME TERRIFIED. Truly. I was freaked the frack out. My husband and I moved up our entire "plan" for children due to that stranger's admonition.

With each of my pregnancies, that doctor moved up and up and up in my book as the legitimate soothsayer. My pressures were indeed a sticky wicket. Week after week and ultrasound after ultrasound, my rock star team, a midwife and a perinatologist, kept a close eye on the bun, the oven, and the amount of heat we were all being subjected to.

All of our boys were delivered a bit early. All of them were pretty teensy tiny. And each time, my blood pressure caused my body to make us all a little more concerned.

Medication. Medical technology. A team of doctors. It was very clear to me by the time I hit 30-years-old that my genes and my conditions were very well-monitored and even mostly managed in the 21st century. But the Oregon Trail, for me, would have been Bad News Bears.

I would not have survived on the Oregon Trail.

I should not have been surprised when a lump showed up on my chest at 33. I should have reminded myself that I was no stranger to medical interventions being necessitated by the introduction of odd circumstances at odd times.

Instead, on the day when I walked into the office where I would experience my first-ever and also, interestingly enough, last-ever mammogram, I had forgotten about my body's familiarity with technology and testing. And so, when my name was called and my husband and I both stood up and were then informed that I'd have to go it alone, I cried. Again. I tried to broker a deal to bend the rule of it being a "female only area" telling them he'd seen my boobs before. I even attempted to state the obvious, that men, also, have breasts. But it was for not. I had to ride solo on this. And leave my always-there-rollaway guy behind.

For the second time that day, I changed into a hospital gown. The tech questioned me about the suspect in question, the lump that was about to make its first big screen debut.

I felt completely defensive and confused. *Am I answering these questions correctly?* I wondered.

"Yes. I have smoked six times," I told her.

"Like, for six years?"

"No, six-ish times in college, I think. I counted. I think that's about right."

"Oh. Okay. So no smoking. No family history of cancer. Three live births. Four pregnancies. Chronic hypertension. Wow...you're so young for that."

Yes. I would not have survived on the Oregon Trail, I thought. I mm-hmmed as she felt the mass. My boobs, which had been primarily plumped for milking for 3.5 out of the last 7 years, were, to me, laughable. I'm fairly certain they were vying for a position as co-chairs of the Itty Bitty Titty Committee. In fact, they were so small that when I felt the lump initially, part of me thought it was likely that I was just feeling a bone from my chest.

She began to place little stickers on my girls and I tried, per my usual go-to defense mechanism, to keep the mood light. I offered a joke about the stickers looking like additional nipples and how handy that would be. Just as a smile returned to my face for a moment, she said, "Ooooh. The skin stretches. Has it always felt like that?"

It stretches? I don't know. I have no idea. Are they supposed to be stretchy? Is this a trick question?

My stomach hurt. I had a bad feeling I was en route to Vomit City. The questions and the stickers and the stretching...it was all too real. And yet I felt totally out of reality. I was nauseous. Dizzied. I needed to get this over with. I needed to get my set smooshed, take my tit pics, and get on with my evening plans.

I stood up and walked over to the mammomonster. The woman warned me that it could be painful as the machine compressed my boob into a tenderized chicken breast. And so the process began. I didn't find it painful in the slightest. And although getting my itter-bitters held in between the paddles was quite a feat, the tech was able to get two scans of each side and with that, we were done.

I sat in the room with my sticker-bedazzled-bosom as the tech consulted with the radiologist. And then she returned.

"We're going to take a few more pictures of the right side."

This is a portion of my story that I like to call: Ashli loses her shit.

"What?!? Why?! Why? I want my husband. I want him. Can't he please just come be with me?"
"I'm sorry. It's a female-only area," the woman reminded me again, very patiently.
"Please! Please! He's my person," I said, tears rolling down my face, once again.
"I guess I could go ask," she offered.
"Never mind. Let's just get it over with," I said.

I was officially at lunatic status. I think she was worried I might start going all Hulk Smash in the room if we didn't get these additional snaps taken soon. It wasn't until those were complete that she told me I'd be going into another room for an ultrasound.

I had a seat with my husband. We sat in another waiting area, him in his suit. Me, in my hospital gown. And guess what? I cried. And honestly, if I had to timestamp my realization, the moment that I lost a whole lotta hope, it was at that point when I thought, *Holy fucking shit. I HAVE CANCER.*

But I didn't yet know for sure.

The ultrasound, administered by a radiologist alongside Dr. S and Adam, gave another glimpse into the goings-on in Miss Righty. The radiologist calmly and very technically explained what we were looking at through the ultrasound imaging. He walked us through my mammogram images. The lump was, in fact, a palpable superficial mass (the technical term for "we can totally feel it by feeling you up") but on the imaging, there was no outline of an actual tumor.

I exhaled. This was surely good news. This was the moment where I could start laughing at my gross overreaction to the events of the day.

"But, if you look here, and here...do you see this?" He pointed to what appeared to be a snow globe happening in my right breast. "These are called 'microcalcifications.' A lot of people, specifically those with dense breast tissue, have microcalcifications. They're perfectly normal and harmless. Yours are what we'd label as 'clustered microcalcifications.'"

I didn't have a stinkin' clue what we were looking at. Countless white splotches speckled the black film image. As I compared the left to the right, it was easy to surmise, even without any schooling, that similar to the moment where I sat amidst the Early Evening Diner's Club in my doctor's office circa 1999 when my blood pressure was being unruly, *one of these things just didn't belong here...one of these things just wasn't the same.* Internally, one of my breasts, the right one, the one with the lump, was not like the left. This was surely *not* good news.

The next step would be a biopsy.

A biopsy. *A biopsy would tell us for sure,* they told me. It was the next step to determine what this little snowstorm was up to. I could get in on Tuesday. The Tuesday following Labor Day. Four days. One long weekend. And then a biopsy. Easy peasy, chicken cheesy.

"Go enjoy your weekend. Don't let this worry you," they said and sent me back out into the world with a billion and one fears racing through my mind.

"What do you think it is?" I asked my doctor again.

"It could be a lot of things. An infection. An adenoma. We know it isn't a cyst. Now we just need to figure out what it is. Of course, I'm concerned. That is why we'll get to the bottom of it."

Adam and I left, and as we headed downtown to the wedding reception I cried on the phone to my parents. I realize how dramatic I was being given the data points up to that moment. From what I'd been told, far more biopsies of abnormalities come back negative for cancer than positive.

But there was this thing I knew. This thing that I'd gathered in my first 33 years. I would not have survived on the Oregon Trail. I would have died of a heart attack as a teenager. I would have died of a stroke as an expectant mother. I would have died, as my children have educated me, of exhaustion. Definitely in the postpartum phase.

If this was cancer, how the hell was I going to survive?

As one might be able to guess, I cried more that evening. I cried telling two of my very best friends, Missy and Kacie, and Nick, in the bar at the reception venue. I cried holding Adam's hand during the bride and groom dance. My emotional wellbeing was dismal. My highs and lows were like a jump rope swinging round and round and up and down. I was in a bigger upheaval of emotions than I had been at six days post-childbirth when I was wearing ginormapads and crying every time I heard a Jack Johnson song. I was officially a complete and utter *mess*.

And then.

AWWWW! NO. NO. NO! I knew those lyrics. I could name that tune in four notes for gosh sakes. My ears were getting "I Hope You Dance"-d. This was no good.

Listen. I am a big Lee Ann Womack fan. She seems like a nice person. "I Hope You Dance" is a perfectly appropriate, lovely, sentimental song to commemorate a heartfelt moment on the dance floor at a wedding. It was not, however, the most ideal tune for the current level of batshit crazy I'd reached.

I excused myself, fearful that the chest-pounding pulse that was rapidly increasing would cause me to explode. The last thing I wanted to do was explode all over the reception of my friend Diana's wedding. Her dress would be ruined. Cancer or none, no one would ever forgive me that.

I retreated to the bathroom. I looked at the girl in the mirror and felt drunk. Have you ever been drunk? If not, kudos to you. If so, travel down this road with me for a second. If you've ever been drunk and looked at yourself in the mirror, have you ever felt sort of separate from yourself? I can recall at least two times in my early twenties where after having far too many adult-strength beverages, I found myself standing at a bathroom sink, washing my hands, only to look up and feel foggy about the person in the reflection. Which is exactly how I felt that night as I looked at the girl in the mirror.

Earlier that week, this person had felt like a grown-ass woman, mother-to-three, wife. Now she looked like a child. A young girl who just wanted someone to tell her that life was all good and here was a lollipop and go play on the swings and be carefree. Makeup was smeared down her face. She was unwound and undone. She was so sad and so desperately aching for her day to have gone differently. I looked at the sad girl. The sad, scared, girl. Only she wasn't a girl. I knew she wasn't just *somebody else*. She was someone I knew better than anyone. She was a daughter. A mother. A wife. A sister. She was *me*. And this two-centimeter lump that had popped up in my life had somehow grown bigger than anything else on my path.

There is no way, no how, no chance that I would have survived on the Oregon Trail. My wheels were already falling off at the tiniest bump. I would have been rendered helpless against the true scourge of the trail—cholera, dysentery, the flu. And the idea of *me*, this helpless, broke down broad, being strong and tough and badass enough to ford the river? Nope.

I walked out of the bathroom and Adam was there. *OF COURSE HE WAS BECAUSE HE'S MAGIC.* He looked at me. And, as if we were replaying the scene of a '90s rom-com, he wiped the tears and smudges from my face. He told me that this was not the end of me unless I let it be.

We walked around the corner and back into the room. I walked out on the dance floor and with a group of my *sisters* we formed a circle around the real focus of the day, the bride. We swayed back and forth, singing Allison Krause. I smiled. Through tears, of course. But I smiled because I realized that I had already had a great life. I smiled because the women I looked at around the circle—several of them the very closest of my close—had been through some big stuff together.

38

Real stuff.

Real life.

Final exams, finding jobs, finding where we fit. Making memories, making fools of ourselves, making ourselves into grownups. Marriages, divorces, babies. Infertility, insecurities, indecision. And every episode of Sex and the City. I'd been on their treks. They'd been on mine. And I knew that they, and so many others, would help me get my wheels back on to travel *any* path I ended up taking.

The Oregon Trail would not have been for me. I don't need to play the game to know my fate. The chronic conditions and my deep need for flavored coffee beans would have done me in. I'm fairly certain of that. But we are not pioneers. We are alive in a time of great research, advancements, and technology, which can often be so completely life-saving. Rarely, in this day and age, are we the first to take on a life-threatening challenge. And if we do, rarely are we called to face it alone.

I did manage, at some point between Allison Krause and a second glass of wine, to take a breath and settle down. I managed to laugh with my girls and be in love with my husband. Even in the most dark of days, these people were my light. Feeling comfort in being with them after a day of chaos, on a night when I otherwise would have stayed home wallowing and watching Gilmore Girls, made me grateful.

I realized that I was not being asked to survive on the Oregon Trail. My life had already necessitated medical interventions. I had been quite used to saying yes to them. And I so far, I'd survived. I had already proven through life and childbirth that I took medical direction quite well. I had made lemons into Summer Beer (aka Strip and Go Naked, aka it tastes kinda like lemonade but realllllly *adulty* lemonade), time and time again. I had already been through poking and prodding, tests and tubes, MRIs and EKGs. And up until that point, I'd done it with sarcasm, humor, and joy.

If this lump in my breast was cancer or some other sort of bump in the road, I wasn't about to let a river of crap tip my wagon. At least not to take over the entire *journey.* Because I wasn't a pioneer, I was a grown-ass woman. It didn't matter one lick if I could survive the Oregon Trail. Even through tears, fears, and Summer Beers with my squad, my God, and medical interventions, I knew that night that no matter how long my life was from then on out, I would rock my modern-day life. And somehow, we'd get through the lumps, bumps, and the storms...I just might have to tie my horse to a couple of wagons to do it.

LESSON:

Sometimes It Takes All the King's Horses

*I*t was a phone call.
Okay. A *bunch* of phone calls.

That's not how it goes on TV. Usually, it's a meeting. In a room. With a big fancy desk.

I was 33 and had been sitting atop a perfectly comfortable place in my world with an excellent view ahead of me, but from the moment I felt a lump in my breast, I'd had a lump in my throat. The phone calls mounted.

Some from my doctor, a GP (technical acronym for general practitioner. Or PCP, primary care physician. Or family practice doctor, aka the type of doctor who has seen it all.), Sandyha Saxena, a woman who I'd known at that point, both as a doctor and a family friend, for several years. A woman who knew my health, my happiness, and my medical history. A woman who had just the right mixture of knowledge and intuition. *The* woman who said, "This lump, it could be nothing. But let's just make sure it's nothing." A woman who I now credit with setting into motion a series of unfortunate-yet-fortunate events because without her, my cancer could have gone undiagnosed for longer than it had.

The phone calls mounted.

There were calls from a woman named Deb, who, up until that point in *my* existence, hadn't existed. Deb, an oncology nurse navigator (technical term for a nurse who navigates you through the life-bomb of cancer fact-finding), updated me as I hung out on a ledge between *life as I knew it* and *cancer-life*. They called it *the gathering stage*.

Somewhere between five to ten times over the course of three weeks, I picked up my phone and Deb told me something new about my boobs. She told me details about the *inside* of the outside I looked at every morning. She told me news about the findings from mammograms, biopsies, ultrasounds, and blood vials. I both loved Deb and feared her. When I saw her number appear on my phone, my nose began to tingle. Yes. My nose. And then my heart would beat as if it was being played by Will Farrell yelling, "More Cowbell!"

Several times, I phoned her. Generally sobbing. Sometimes hyperventilating. Hopeful that perhaps I'd call and she'd say, "We don't have you in our records, you crazy nutjob. You must have just imagined all of that. Go back to your life."

But the tests and gathering stage continued. The one word I held tight to was *inconclusive*. Inconclusive meant maybe it was a malignancy or maybe it wasn't. Maybe it was stage 0 (or ductal carcinoma in situ, aka DCIS) or maybe it wasn't. Maybe it was further along or maybe it wasn't. I heard it time after time in the first two weeks of testing. The inconclusive results were both maddening *and* the floatation device that was keeping my mind from completely drowning in despair.

Each time Deb called, I felt it necessary and self-preserving to explain to her that I wasn't usually so out of my mind. I wasn't always crying. I didn't always stalk people I'd never even met. But

I had these boys and this husband and this whole plan to be alive until I was wrinkly and saggy and this whole "gathering" situation was really eating into the picture I'd had of *happily ever after.*

The gathering stage felt like I was stuck in an old-fashioned viewfinder, slowly being clicked through to the next day with everything blurry and muddled, each picture making me squint to see if I could still see myself in my *before* life.

Three weeks of clicking through a blur of anguish and debilitating anxiety. Of blood work. Of peeing in cup after cup with my two-year-old staring at me confused as I prepped the area and produced the sample. Of my first mammogram. In fact, my only mammogram. Of my first, second, and third breast ultrasounds. Of one biopsy. Of another. Of telling myself that there was no way it was cancer and also, congruently, that I definitely had cancer and was going to die.

And then my future came clearly into view with *the* phone call.

When you see it in the movies or on a TV show, the news "You have cancer" always seems to be delivered from some very distinguished-looking individual in a white coat behind a large-fancy-person Mahogany desk in an office with carpet and window drapes and natural light peeking through just enough to cast a Gingham filter on the magnitude of the situation. The doctor holds a chart in front of them and after delivering the news, the patient and often a companion, sit across from them in shock.

Instead of sitting in a room, after all of the findings had been wrapped up nicely into one package labeled, "*Contains shittiness,*" Deb called and said, "Well. Do you have a few minutes to chat?" It was in that chatting that she very softly but surely delivered the news that I imagine she'd had to share time and time again, phone call after phone call: "This mass in your breast, it *is* a malignancy."

After she said, "It *is* a malignancy. It's in your breast," I very unsteadily questioned, "What if it's *everywhere*? How do we know? If it is, *then what*? Am I going to die?"

43

She paused. She had done this before. She knew what I, a 33-year-old-mother and wife was actually asking was, *"Am I going to die **soon**?"*

Her voice was calm. She was just as patient as she'd been over the last three weeks as she began to introduce me to *my breast cancer.*

She told me they had identified a two-centimeter mass in my right breast with no physical evidence of it having spread to the lymph nodes.

Deb explained to me that doing a biopsy in a breast is similar to sticking a toothpick into raisin toast. Yes. Raisin toast. Picture yourself sticking a toothpick into raisin toast. Sometimes, you hit a raisin. Sometimes, you don't. Now. Picture that the toast is a boob (I know, you'll never look at toast the same again). And the raisins are the weird cells. As they perform a biopsy, they are poking into a mass or a cluster of cells, hopeful to hit the raisin and determine that it is, indeed a raisin (*errrrr,* a benign occurrence), and not cancer.

But. Mine was not a rogue raisin or even a grape that had lodged itself into my chest cavity. The tissue samples showed existence of cancer floating around in my breast.

She told me it appeared to be early stage—1, 2, or 3.

They very much believed it to be contained within the breast or just barely locally spread to the lymph nodes.

She explained it was labeled as triple positive, which meant that my tumor had fed on or grown from two hormones and one protein that all female bodies make: estrogen, progesterone, and human epidermal growth factor receptor 2 (aka, Her2+).

It was identified to be both DCIS (ductal carcinoma in situ or Stage 0 breast cancer) and as early-stage Angiolymphatic Invasion (sometimes called Vascular or Lymphovascular Invasion) meaning the cancer cells they had been able to pinpoint through biopsy were located in the lymph spaces of my breast. She explained that when cancer is growing in these spaces, there is absolutely a chance that it has spread outside the breast but it does not always mean that.

Clear as mud, right?

She told me that I'd been assigned a *multidisciplinary team* (a technical and *fancy pants* term to describe a team of medical professionals who have different areas of knowledge and work together to kick ass on behalf of a patient). And that, on a day in the very near future, should I choose to proceed in their care, I would meet in person and go through their suggested treatment plan.

She was very compassionate. She listened to me. She answered my questions, each one. We were on the phone for over an hour.

In addition to phone calls from Deb, were calls in desperation to Adam. Me, heaving air in and out, him, silent but there. He listened to me falling down, knowing that no amount of him telling me it would be okay would make me believe it.

There were calls to my mom, begging her to tell me that in her 35 years in oncology (the technical term for cancer), she had most definitely heard of all the things they were sharing with me. That this was all sort of *normal* in the world of cancer fact-finding in a 33-year-old female.

Then there were calls to a friend of my mom's, Catherine. I added her in my phone as *Angel Nurse* (seriously). For the first three weeks, I texted and called her daily. Multiple times, daily, to be more accurate.

My siblings. Family. Framily. These communities of people who had become characters in my pages. They were with me—in my home, on my phone, at my door, on my blog—almost as if sitting Shiva during my period of mourning. My brother would call me and I would laugh. My sister would call and I would apologize for opening the breast cancer box in our family. I would talk to my dad and sob. My mother-in-law, Kathy, would call and we'd pray.

I had been sitting on the wall. Waiting on the in-between. Would I be able to go back to the side of my life that had not been stained by cancer? Or would I have to lower down to the other side?

After the first week of gathering, we knew enough to know it was cancer. We knew this because of the team who now knew two centimeters of me better than I knew most any part of myself. And I knew that I was falling.

It was my great fall. At least at that point, it was the biggest *cracking open* I'd experienced and I was too pained and sad to try to hold my arms just so to cover the jags and crags that were splitting the seams of my exterior.

Everyone could see it. I was exposed.
For three weeks, the gathering went on.
Gathering results.
Gathering research.
Gathering my present and my potential future.

And then, it was D-Day. Diagnosis day. The day that Adam and I sat stationary as a revolving door of doctors, nurses, and people holding my medical chart and my future, entered, explained, listened, and exited. By the end of the day, I'd met a whole new cast of characters in my story. This team that had been assembled for me.

My oncologist, a young brilliant physician named Dr. Tandra. *My* surgical oncologist, Dr. Thayer, a moxie'd medical wiz who was beautifully versed in her knowledge of women and cancer. *My* radiation oncologist, Dr. Wahl, a mop-topped intellect who, though he looked to be just fresh out of undergrad, was in fact, around my age and quite impressive in his field. *My* nurse navigator, Deb.

Mine. My team. How did I suddenly have *my* team?

Oh yes. I'd fallen off the wall.

Three weeks prior, I'd been sitting contently as a mom, a wife, a daughter, and on and on. And then I started falling.

46

For three weeks, I was suspended in-flight. Falling down. Falling apart. And it was the phone call that confirmed that yes, in fact, I had cancer, that smashed me to bits and shards. From what used to feel shiny and intact, I fell. It wasn't *pretty*. It wasn't graceful.

I was a modern-day Humpty-Dumpty. No, not an egg wearing pants (that's just really weird, honestly. I mean, funny. But weird, right?). But a person who'd been sitting comfortably in a familiar place in my life. And then...

I fell.

We all fall. At some point, we fall from our spot, thrown off-balance by the hard somethings. Then we look at all of our pieces in disarray, spread out from their normal positions. We look through the viewfinder, searching for answers as to how to get back up. How to get back on the wall. How to put ourselves back together again.

I knew, as *my team* educated me on my breast cancer (there are so many different types. And there are so many different treatment plans depending on your type and your age and your staging), it was the moment. The one where we were officially on the other side of the wall. Where I wouldn't be *going back* to my *before*.

This team so patiently and confidently shared with me and educated me on my diagnosis. They explained that because I had a two-centimeter tumor in my right breast—and that tumor, pathologically, was Triple Positive—it was recommended that I be treated with chemotherapy (or as those of us in the know refer to it: "chemo"), undergo a mastectomy (or as those who have a sense of humor like me refer to it: "get my boobs emptied out"), and also, receive radiation (or as I like to call it: "get zapped").

I clung to Adam's hand, barely believing that this was where our vows had landed him. Still, we breathed a sigh of relief over having knowledge. Knowing what the *something* was and knowing how we would fight it felt calming to my nerves.

I'm not sure if the anti-anxiety medication I'd added into my daily routine just a week and a half prior had finally begun to take the punch out of my fear. It could have been that the prayer and passages and mantras that had been on repeat in my mind had reduced the control I felt I needed to have. Regardless of the cause, the effect left me feeling calmer than I had in three weeks' time.

I knew we'd have to walk out the doors that we came in through. And I knew I'd be walking out as a cancer patient. I knew we'd have to share the news. I knew we'd have phone call after phone call to explain it all to our family. I knew we'd have to tell our boys. *OH DEAR GOODNESS, how do we do this part of parenting?* But at least now, after hearing the explanation, and the game-plan, when I shared our news — *our*, because while it was in my body, it was about to be in so many people's lives — I could give them facts. Truths. Plans.

The problem still existed that I was broken. And I knew I needed all the king's horses. And probably all the king's men (and women, duh). I needed the team I'd been assigned, and to them I'd add tens of nurses and aides and receptionists who would provide a continuity of care. I needed my family. My Framily. My squad. I needed my friends. I needed to be able to be broken as everything felt shattered. And I needed to, take a deep breath and allow myself to be put back together again.

When we break. When we bust. When we fall. We can piece a life together following the impact. It may not ever be put together the way we remember it. It may take longer than we ever want it to.

Sometimes we find ourselves in a place of feeling so broken, so certain it's impossible to ever mend our cracks. Feeling so torn and desperate to find some semblance of wholeness again. That is, I believe, why we were given community. Why we walk this earth in time with so many others. Others who are the joy through our suffering. That is why we are never told we have to go it alone. That is why we get to lean on others to reassemble us, at least until we are ready to reassemble ourselves. And eventually, we may actually find a place on top of a wall without feeling like we will topple right back down.

The nursery rhyme says, "Humpty Dumpty sat on a wall. Humpty Dumpty had a great fall. All the king's horses and all the king's men, *couldn't* put Humpty together again."

BUT.

Spoiler alert: My fall, it was great. Greatly damaging and destructive. Greatly life-altering. Greatly terrifying. And yet, greatly changing. The fall broke me. Busted me. Left me feeling like the top of the wall was far too high for me to ever scale alone.

But with all the king's horses and all the king's men (again, and WOmen)—my team, my people—guess what? They were there in every valley, right alongside me over the mountains, splashing through the rivers. And eventually, even if different than I'd planned, I found my life coming together back again.

LESSON:

I Am Not in Control

Hi, my name is Ashli and I'm a recovering control freak. (Go ahead, give me a little, "*Hi Ashli*" back.)

What about you? Are you a fan of control? Do you like when it feels like all your ducks are just so nicely lined up, waddling around with their cute little duff feathers wiggling in unison? Are you a person who has, on more than a few (or a thousand) occasions proudly declared, "I'm just such a planner!"

Oh, *control*. It's so *nice-to-have*, isn't it? Planning. Feeling organized.

It's nice to feel like all the moving parts are lining up nicely *just so*. That the *plan* is all coming together. That putting in the groundwork of planning and strategizing and goal-setting is a completely useful expenditure of time. That all the scraps of paper (some in my purse. Some in one notebook. One on the back of a receipt...) reminding me what is done and what is still yet to-do are completely necessary for being the most effective human being I can be.

Oh dear goodness gravy. THAT'S ALL PRETTY MUCH HOG-WASH. Except the scraps of papers with "to-do" and check boxes. Those are legit real.

In the area of organization, I leave quite a bit to be desired. I'm pretty much the polar opposite of Monica Gellar. In the area of control, I am recovering from the need to feel like I need it. But it's been quite the process to get here.

I don't remember always being a planner. Rather, I've been more of a fly-by-the-seat-of-my-pants-er. My career as Development Director necessitated hot planning action. Events and budgets. Committees and strategery. I began to think in cycles of events—a world where it really does behoove one to have all the i's dotted and t's crossed.

I slowly learned that having control of my day made it easier to put out fires. I learned that if I controlled the messaging correctly, it led to better rapport and relationships. I learned that if I forecasted appropriately, it made my job less stressful. At work, through my ability to control, I found success.

And next came pregnancy. The planning and preparation that takes place throughout a modern-day gestation period is just wild. I had my first babe on the Brehm before the existence of letter boarded announcements, babymoons, and gender reveals. But there were still details to manage—a place for the baby to sleep, getting the car seat in just-so, and scheduling pregnancy photos for *just* the right time in the pregnancy where the belly was clearly more than just a large cheeseburger and fries from the night before but not yet a large animal burrowing about trying to bust out of its cage.

After eight months of harboring a human, we got to meet the little mister. Suddenly, control, if there had been any left by the end of my pregnancy, grew wings and flew right out the door of the hospital and didn't get buckled into our car.

This person we'd just met, a four pound nine ounce fresh-to-the-earth human, ruled the school. From sleep to eating to our DVR binging habits, it was clear that I was going to need to loosen my grip a bit on the *need* for control because it just wasn't gonna happen.

Slowly, we gained back our hold on the reigns and became the Alpha Dogs in our family unit. Then we added another kid. And another one. Because what else should you do when you are trying to pretend you are in control than have more children?

Over a seven-year-sprint we vacillated between being a complete and utter shitshow to having perfectly scheduled and aligned naps, bedtime procedures, feeding routines, and the like. Over and over again, I stated, "It's just easier. It's just easier to keep a schedule and routine. It's just easier to have some *delusion* of control."

Do you feel me on that? Do you feel like if you just left plans and days to the wind, you'd never accomplish anything? Are you a person who thrives with order and a plan?

I think it's totally human to want control or even feel like we *need* it, just as we *need* water, food, air, and a shower every so often.

But I also think it could be highly beneficial for you to repeat after me: I am pretty much mostly not in control.

Go ahead. I'll give you a moment.

I am pretty much mostly not in control.

How do I know this? Because of the wildebeest.

Cancer was not in my plans. Cancer at 33, after birthing three boys, and having such small boobs that I was pretty certain my nipples were just gripping on for dear life to a mountain that had lost all its holds, was not *even* on my radar. It wasn't included in my forecasting or brainstorming sessions. In my controlled life and universe, cancer had not been offered a seat until it walked

52

right in and kicked out the things that had achieved first-row status. It was a shock and awe campaign. And I was most certainly shocked. And in awe.

Then came a glimmer of familiarity: a plan. My treatment plan. YES. They gave me the plan and I held onto that sucker like it was my roadmap. To kickoff "The Great Cancer Ass Kicking" of 2015-2016, I would first undergo six rounds of chemo. One round of four drugs every three weeks. That would be 18 weeks. 18 weeks. I could do this.

And so we followed the plan. I had my first round of chemotherapy and crossed it off my list of to-dos'. I looked ahead, *onward and upward*, I told myself. *This is all going just loverly.*

But then came the Wildebeest.

Dagnabit.

First, it was not truly a wildebeest. I'm certain anyone in the medical profession would be less than thrilled if patients started calling in to say, "I think I have a wildebeest." Instead, the term to describe the armpit accessory that popped up following a biopsy procedure, is a seroma. Instead of walking around singing "Ma ma ma my seroma" 24/7, I decided to name this visitor the Wildebeest.

To be perfectly honest, I flippantly chose the moniker Wildebeest because I was thinking it was a type of R.O.U.S (Rodents of Unusual Size for those who have never seen The Princess Bride. Also, if you've never seen The Princess Bride, I find that inconceivable.) when in all reality, an actual wildebeest is more like an ox with a beard.

But *my* wildebeest was a lump of fluid that, in its largest state, was bigger than both of my breasts combined. Again, while that is not a great explanation of anything *large*, to paint a clearer picture, it was like half of a softball had put down roots in my armpit. And it hurt.

The Wildebeest was *not* in my roadmap. It was *not* in my plans. And I could not oust the beest. It was mostly in control of itself. *Awesome.*

The Wildebeest was simply a harbinger of things to come. Two days post-chemo, chills and fever took me to the emergency room. Those symptoms were due to something called *neutropenic fever,* which means that white blood cell counts are too low and you're due for a tune-up.

I was not in control, *DAMN IT.*
I thought I was in control once I had all of my kids on a nap schedule.
I thought I was in control once our family budget was revamped.
I thought I would for sure be *in control* once I turned from my 20s to 30s.
And then I thought I'd regained control with the roadmap and the treatment plan.

Nope.

Those complications in my first round of chemo sent me nose-diving into a pit of anxiety. I can recall sitting on my stairs, tears falling, snot dripping, face pricked with the heat of fear. My mother-in-law stood near me as I talked about how I was scared that every round was going to go like this. I was worried that the chemo wouldn't work. I was terrified that I'd always have a third boob in my armpit even after they removed the original gals.

"I just feel like I don't have any control," I said.

She told me, "You don't." There was more discussion. As usual, she provided a calm I so needed and wisdom I didn't possess. But the two words, *you don't,* those were just right.

She was right. I didn't have control over the circumstances. I couldn't make the Wildebeest go back to its home. I couldn't control my body's reaction to chemo. I couldn't control so much of it.

What could I adjust? My expectations. I could offer myself a heaping dose of chill-the-freak-out and stop *trying* to have control. Because the reality was, trying was exhausting. And not a good use of my good time.

It was a reminder to me that there can be a balance in control and letting go. There can be a balance between planning and living in the present. And for me, there needed to be a major overhaul on my expectations.

Jobs, trying to have babies, raising kids, marriage, the Wildebeest...life is made up of a million bajillion things that are completely above our pay grade.

The only thing. The *only* thing. *The* only thing. (Yes, it is *that* important that I needed to say it three times). The only thing that I've been able to fairly consistently take control of is my attitude. And even that can be dicey some days and some ways.

As my life built up into its first 33 years, there were endless examples that proved I was not really the one running my show. But I kept telling myself, *"When..."* When I stay home I'll feel like I have a handle on the house stuff. When I go back to work, I'll feel more content. When I am done having babies, I will organize those drawers. But seriously, *why*?

What if instead of planning every moment of everything, we left a little more up to where the day takes us and a little less of *exactly how I think this is supposed to go*? What would happen?

I'm not suggesting you don't ever set an alarm clock, stop going to work, never do another load of laundry (because there will always be laundry), or let your fridge go empty and start living off of pop-tarts (but really. Have you had a pop-tart lately? They are delicious.). I'm not telling people to be slobs or irresponsible. But I think there is something to be said for reminding yourself on occasion, after a deep inhale and exhale, that this hiccup or this part that you didn't *plan* for is not your end, it is only a new beginning you didn't have on the calendar.

When we can accept and expect—accept that we don't have a crystal ball and expect that shit's gonna happen—our falling down can lead to an easier get-back-up-again.

I don't make plans anymore. Well, that's not completely accurate. I have mad meal planning skillz. I have dreams and hopes of some great future vacays and seeing every state in the USA with our boys. But planning every minute of my day or expecting that my children will know exactly where their left shoe is or that I will just magically always be healthy? I don't expect those things.

I still believe that this life of mine is one bang-up, good time. I haven't lost hope or optimism in life. But I have had to remind myself that I'm not in control of much. My Wildebeest, while no longer in my armpit, will long live in a corner of my mind to remind me that if there is something we can always be sure of it is that we can't really be all that sure or certain of anything.

You may encounter a wildebeest. Yours hopefully won't be in your armpit. Or be a seroma. But you will have times where you are met with the reality that you are not in control. This may cause you to completely break down. (Note: that is still and always will be a completely acceptable reaction.) But, you can also remind yourself daily that some of the best things come out of moments that we never expect. A wildebeest might initially look like a big, terrifying R.O.U.S. until you will realize that it is actually a friendly ox with a beard all along and was only meant to add some character to your story.

LESSON:

I Am Normally Abnormal

Abnormal cells.

That's the wording my husband used when we told our Oldest that cancer had decided to set up a mingling session in my boob. He said, very steadily and matter-of-factly, "We wanted to talk to you...Mommy has cancer...cancer is when the normal cells in the body start acting abnormally and you have to get rid of the cells."

It went well in the moment. In fact, the kid asked if he could play Wii and have a snack. Having just listened to my husband tell my 7-year-old that his mommy had cancer, the kid could have asked for a merry-go-round to be installed in our backyard and I would have acquiesced. He left the room, grabbed some sort of packaged food and resumed his Wii adventures. I tucked my husband's wording of my current life happenings into my brain to use as salt for any mental grease fires that might shoot up over the months that were ahead of me. (Fun fact: some people think you should throw flour on a fire, but apparently salt is the real deal.)

Abnormal cells.

Looking at it that way, I thought, ...*and I was surprised*?

I've always been weird. In fact, I'd even say that I've been on such a steady streak of being weird that to me, weird is what's normal. Why, on earth, had I felt so jarred by the reality that my weirdness had settled all the way to the cellular level?

When I talked with Dr. S shortly after we began the cancer-diagnosing expedition, she looked at me and very firmly said, "You are having normal fears. Normal reactions. But I need you to start to act abnormally. Your body will heal better."

She's a smart cookie, that lady. Also, cookies sound delicious.

She was spot on. The anxiety I was carrying was creating more issues than I needed to bring on and it was time for me to figure out how to move from being a newly diagnosed cancer patient to being a cancer survivor.

Abnormal behavior. Being my weird, wacky self. That's what I needed.

Again. Weird. Nutty. Call it what you like. I have always been abnormal. Ask any of my high school classmates and I think they'd agree...I have always been quirky...different...abnormal. Loud. Inappropriate. Sarcastic. In love with grammar (I blame my sister, Danielle, and my dad for that oddity). A big lover. A big feeler. But I like to think I've always sort of embraced my personality. In my family, I was never going to vie for the title of the smartest or the most successful or the most talented. My brother and sister cornered the market on those with their big brains and wicked skills. But me, I could be the weird one. I could be *myself*. And luckily, my family loved me because of it.

It wasn't until my college years that I began to feel more secure with my abnormalness. Like a good portion of the population, I still cared about what people thought of me. But if they thought I was *too much* then I knew that for them, I probably was. And that was okay. I began to worry less about what I wasn't and started embracing what I was...*me*.

58

Fast forward through my twenties and stop the tape at age 33. If you don't know what "stop the tape is," than congratulations on never having had to set the VCR to record 90210 every Thursday while you were at dance class or manually wind a cassette when the tape came out of your favorite Debbie Gibson single. Now where were we.... oh yes, 33.

Me. 33. Abnormal. Weird. And dun-dun-DUNNNNN! Cancer.

Cancer is also abnormal. While it feels as if you can't throw a rock out your front door without hitting a person who has dealt with it, cancer is not the norm. It is not the status quo. So how are we supposed to know how to handle it?

Honestly, though, how are we supposed to handle anything?

Miscarriage. Infertility. Mental illness. Divorce. A hip replacement. A kid throwing a fit on the floor of a restaurant. How are we supposed to handle the unexpected?

There's no *one* right way because there's no *one* right human.

Almost as immediately as I heard the words *"You need a mammogram,"* I became aware of the fact that just as I'd approached motherhood, faith, pregnancy, politics, marriage, and the last season of Gilmore Girls based on my own personal ideas and experiences, every single human chooses to tackle cancer differently.

Some people don't want to discuss treatment.
Some people choose to see 17 doctors and fly all over the US to find the place where they will receive their care.
Others decide they want to research and research all on their own.
When I received my diagnosis, I did my very best to stay off of Google and take my news as it came.

There are many who would like to try and go about their life per usual. And then there was me... the girl who put her boobs on the Internet.

I decided that if I'd been abnormal up until I knew about the abnormal cells, I might as well just keep on keepin' on. After all, a life-shaking diagnosis was no time to change my fundamental makeup.

In every little and big thing we do in our lives, each of us gets to choose how we take on a situation. Cancer is no different. I don't think there is a right or wrong way. To share about your health or not is a completely personal decision. To switch doctors a million times? *Your decision.* To have seven revisions of the reconstruction process? *Your decision.* To go on anxiety meds to catch your freakin' breath? *Your decision.*

It's okay to tackle your experience with cancer or adversity or life just like you'd eat an elephant—taking one small bite at a time before you figure out what's next (side note: I've never eaten an elephant and am also a big fan of Dumbo so please don't take the eating of an elephant literally).

Upon diagnosis, there were very well-meaning people who would learn about my treatment plan and question, "You're having chemo first? My sister had breast cancer and had her surgery first."

There were people who would state, "You're not working out through chemo? I would think working out would be so good for your energy level."

There were comments from people who had gone through breast augmentation, assuring me that *at least I would get big perky boobs at the end of it all.*

There were moments where people would share that they knew a person who had cancer at 33 and died. And then reassure me that it was okay because *hers* wasn't breast.

Every single time a person would *question* any part of my journey, I TRULY had to act abnormally instead of reacting to their opinions. Instead of feeling defensive or worried. Instead of taking any part of their statements as a judgment or an attack. I had to take a breath, mentally step away for a moment, and remember that they knew *not* what they were doing or saying. They were trying to provide empathy and sympathy and comfort. For

60

my sanity, every single time a person shared about someone who lost their life to cancer, I had to remind myself that it was their relatable story. Relating to each other is what we know how to do as humans.

You and I are made to react. How we react, how we internalize the words of others is up to each one of us. So I chose to react to those curious statements, those questioning responses, those nuggets of negative outcomes in an *abnormal* way.

I chose to breathe. And to say to myself, "Theirs is not MY story."

When the positives came, when the relating felt more like a cheerleading section, I tucked those into the same spot where I tucked my husband's wording of *abnormal cells*.

Maybe it was a sprinkle of sweet honey for my mind when someone would share, "My mom had cancer when I was 7 and now I'm 35 and she's the best grandma ever." Perhaps the comfort received when a woman in Target would scoot her cart next to mine and smile while relaying, "I lost all my hair three years ago and look at me now! Locks to my shoulders!" Or perhaps it was the jolt of energy that occurred when a friend would remind me, "You can do this hard thing because women are made to be warriors."

Yes, those moments would be held close to my chest for safe keeping with a label that read, *this is my story. I am abnormal. I am weird. And that makes me my own kind of wonderful.*

In all of my weird ways, I would joke about how my boobs were never great anyway. I would remind people that while cancer was obviously complete shit, so was bad traffic or a child screaming, "But I want it!" in the car for 32 minutes while you're trying to drive an entire motor vehicle through a torrential downpour. I decided to go bald on occasions where hot flashes were setting my head aflame. I posted pictures of us having dance parties and celebrations in the middle of the week because it was a Wednesday and I'd never had a truer reminder that Wednesdays and Thursdays and October and in 2018 are made for dancing. I chose to talk about my faith and to pray and to share my spiritual growth as I trudged through the mess of it all. I chose, also, to talk about the goodness I found in it all.

And I decided to share. I decided to be an open book. I decided to bare all on the internet. Well, almost all. I still haven't shown my nipples to the world because I don't need the Internet to flag me as porn. No mama needs that when she plans to have teenagers someday.

But I decided to show pictures of drains. And I decided to name my drains. And my IV pole. And my expanders. Not because all of those things are the *right* way. Because they were *my* way.

We are all doing heavy lifting here.

It's just the truth, and it's one of the most reoccurring lessons I learned through cancer. It's why I have written it OVER and OVER. You're likely like, "Girl. We get it. People have hard stuff." And if you're saying that then I feel like Thomas the Train tooting his horn and touting, *I'm being a very useful engine.* Because the minute we can understand that every person is going through stuff that feels difficult for them, I believe we begin to realize that we do not have a corner on the market of *crap*. Once we realize that, we are able to be nicer humans. And nicer humans produce goodness.

And goodness...ohhhhhh, the goodness. To me, the goodness is the soul-strengthening stuff that makes all the hard parts doable.

It doesn't matter if you're a college student navigating your limbo between high school and the real world or a person pursuing your first job. Maybe you're a never-wants-to-be-married chick or perhaps you tied the knot at 19. You might be a first-time mama or you've birthed four kids and adopted two. You might still have both of your parents or carry the daily grief of having lost someone who was once your world. You might be dying to get pregnant, only to have lost your dream before you could ever see it come into the world. Or perhaps, you are someone who doesn't even know your dream yet. Or maybe you're a 33-year-old woman who gets a life-altering diagnosis.

Based on your life and where you are and how you were raised and what makes up your DNA and what has come before this moment, you will, without even really thinking about it, design your own plan of attack. You will figure out how to get through your shit. You will decide if you want to dance in the kitchen of hide under your covers.

You might be going through something really hard *hard* for your body or mind or life and you might feel the need to lie in bed and binge all every season of Shameless that Netflix has to offer in order to feel better about your own life choices. You may be the type of person who is in a darker phase than you'd like but you don't want to talk about it. You might be a vaguebooker (A person who posts very vague posts on social media which cause people to scratch their heads or ask, "What's going on?") and want people to know that you need prayers or happy vibes but you don't want to talk about it yet. (Admittedly, I previously got highly annoyed by vaguebooking. HOWEVER, I also had to remind myself: *this is their journey* and that there is a reason they're asking for what they're asking for the way they're asking for it.) You might be a person who records an Insta story every day with your 99 problems and cancer ain't one. It's all personal. It's all abnormally normal.

Whatever reality yours is, it is *yours*. No one else is living your actual life. Give yourself a break. Breathe. And in terms of comparing what's yours to what's not, that mission is generally futile. The craziest part of all is that what others may perceive as abnormal likely feels very normal to you, and that, I think, is perfectly acceptable.

Now, don't confuse this lesson with the invitation to be a total asshole to people for your whole life or to never roll up your socks and get on with your jaunt. Wallowing and feeling sorry for yourself can be a choice, but I might warn you that it can only go on for so long before no one else wants to be around anymore because of the toxicity it emits into their world. You are welcome to go your own way, but if you choose to completely go your own way and irritate every person you come into contact with, constantly be negative, and are never open to listening to other humans, that is up to you. But don't be surprised if you often find yourself wallowing and crabbing alone because, as the saying goes, most people "ain't got time for that."

But you can certainly take life's happenings in your own style. There will be occasions for throwing yourself a pity party for one. There will be moments that will feel too hard to muddle through. And there will be moments where the way you are acting may be perceived by others as abnormal. (At some point, common decency is just a good core value to adopt. So it may not serve you well to walk around the local grocery store tits-out holding a boom box playing *In Your Eyes* at every passerby. That is certainly abnormal but might also land you in jail.)

This whole life thing? It's *your* whole life thing. No one else will ever ever ever care as much about your life as you do (except perhaps your mother and your grandma, because specifically grandmas are often made up of a very special mix of magic). No one else will ever know what it is like for *you* to do life...to live your unique set of circumstances...to raise *your* kid...to do *your* job...to sleep next to the love of *your* life...to go through *your* version of hard.

Because you, too, are abnormal. SPOILER ALERT: THERE IS NO NORMAL. There is no manual handed to parents when they leave the hospital to ensure that all people are raised in the same circumstances with the same rules and the same life happenings. There is no tried and true method for living, outside of to keep breathing and don't ignore the need to fart or burp every once in a while (lest we should blow up). We are all attacking each day with our mad skillz and we are all doing it the best way we know how.

Someday, you might even surprise yourself. You might choose to tackle something in a way that you have never done before. You may figure out that what was once your *normal* now feels *abnormal*. You might even realize that you can't even believe who you once were.

It doesn't always matter what happens in the end. Maybe, for you, there is truly no measurable outcome. And it's really just about your in-between. It matters that, in the middle, in the living, in the breaths, you truly lived. You had good days and bad days. You survived highs and lows. You feel like when you survey your journey from a thousand feet overhead, you feel that it is a representation of the life you traveled...and at least in the end you can honestly say, "I am normally abnormal and for me, that is just right."

LESSON:

I Am Not Wonder Woman

When cancer landed on my doorstep, so did mail. Daily, we were flooded with boxes and envelopes from friends, family, and strangers.

When I opened a package from my sorority sister, Carissa, it was a picture perfect fall day and, outside of the fact that I now knew I had cancer in my body, the day had been pretty darn good.

But in the opening of the package, the day took on a sort of magic.

The package contained a Wonder Woman t-shirt. Complete with a cape and a foam crown. I put it on immediately and posed for pictures in my armor.

When the morning of my first chemo arrived, I was terrified. I was scared beyond scared that I was, at 33-years-old, going to be filled up with toxic juice. I was worried that chemo might hurt. I was nervous for the potential aftermath ahead of me—the nausea, the bone aches, the hair starting to go. I was more nervous than a long-tailed cat in a room full of rockin' chairs to *start*. So I put on my armor.

I walked into my first chemo session with hair curled, makeup on, and my Wonder Woman garb protecting my body. To those who were unaware of my day ahead, it might have looked like I was dressed up for Halloween. But I knew that I had to, for my own coping and healing, do the process my way. I would make this fun. My boys and I, we would consider chemo days glorious, because they would be our time to fight. Like little Pac-Men eating up every bit of my disease, chemo would be evicting this horrible unwanted guest. So we would party.

My very first infusion nurse, Denise, could tell I was scared. Even with my costume, she read my nerves. And so she brought in the pharmacists to assuage my fears a bit. I hugged them. These two men I'd only just met, I hugged them out of fear. I hugged them because, as they explained the process of chemo, I started to understand that this part—the infusion—would actually be painless. I would be able to sit and relax over the course of the treatments. Oh, how I immediately loved those people.

Chemo days began to be my jam. That makes me sound deranged, I know. But I began to look forward to them. Not simply because of the fighting. But also because they were days where I often got to see some of my favorite people—friends, family, my pastor, and the doctors and nurses who I claimed as part of my tribe as they helped me combat my disease. Each time chemo day came around, I was on an uphill swing after a downward crash from the therapies. And so, I treated them like a celebration, which meant dressing up for the soiree.

Yes, the Wonder Woman getup set a trend into motion. The second chemo round, I donned a hilariously witty shirt that said, "F*ck Cancer." It had also come in the mail. The Oldest called it my Fix Cancer shirt because it so brilliantly placed a sideways cancer-ribbon in place of the U and the C and the k, making it Fix Cancer to a 6-year-old's eyes. And I wore bracelets. Stacks of them sent by friends and family. My armor to remind me that I was strong and that they were all praying for me. That I could be a badass warrior. I wore earrings too. Big, leather earrings sent by a former-stranger. And a stocking hat. Because wigs just weren't really my thing.

Then came the next round. It was the day after Thanksgiving. It was game day for my football team, The Huskers. I wore a stocking cap that was designed like a cob of corn, Christmas leggings, and again, the Wonder woman gear.

The fourth round it was Christmas time. A holly jolly time of the year. So I wore an elf costume. Complete with a red "Love your Melon" stocking cap to cover my fully bald dome. I took pictures with my boys and we celebrated the joy of the season. The joy of Mama getting past the halfway point of my 20 weeks of treatment. I posed with my oncologist as though I were an Elf on the Shelf—except I was really the Elf on the Exam Table. And the day was so darn wonderful.

The fifth round, I stepped up my game. I wore my high school cheerleading uniform. Well, actually, I had to borrow one from a fellow alumni because I sold mine circa 2000 to buy a pair of Doc Martens. At 33-years-old, I walked into chemo wearing WCHS letters. My husband wore his high school letter jacket. I held a sign thanking all who had been cheering us on.

My girlfriends hung with me that day. We talked about nipples and crotchless panties. My pastor popped in for a visit (right in the middle of the crotchless panties discussion). The day was memorable, and helped me realize what I *had* to wear for my sixth round.

For round number six, after having completed the first five, I pulled out my wedding dress. Why? Because my wedding dress was the outfit I'd worn on what had been the luckiest day of my life. So it only seemed fitting.

The hubs and I walked arm-in-arm. I wore my gown. He wore a top hat and a tuxedo tee, as did our boys. From afar, our nephews also rocked tux tees. Our niece dressed in a fancy dress. A few of my besties surprised me by showing up for the festivities in bridesmaids' dresses. One showed up with cookies. I had a village there that day and the boys and I swung a mallet to sound the "cancer be gong."

I rejoiced. I hugged my village—Adam. Barrett. Jonah. Harrison. Parents. In-laws. Godparents. Sorority sisters. Pastor. Nurses. Doctors. The staff. I thanked God for my dress and the miracles I knew it could work. For the grace it had given me on my wedding day. For every bit of life I'd gotten with Adam since.

We partied after that chemo. A reception of sorts. We toasted. We cheers'd. We laughed. And oh, I cried. Tears of total joy. Because again, it was my party and I could cry if I wanted to.

It was one of the very best days. It could have been terrible. I was receiving toxic sludge. But the beauty came in a different form of wonder. It came from the people. From the vibe. And for me, from the dress.

I am not Wonder Woman. I simply figured out how I could find some wonder and beauty in what everyone referred to as *the battle*.

I suited up.
I showed up.
And I got to survive.

LESSON:

Everyone Needs a Roll Away Person

Just days after I was told that my body had been unfaithful to me—secretly taking normal cells, converting them to cancer, and grouping together in my boob—I had to undergo a sentinel node biopsy.

I am not a doctor. Let me just get that outta the way and from here on out we can all understand that I am not a doctor and any sort of medical jargon or information that I share is pretty anecdotal, okay? Cool.

So the sentinel node biopsy. This is a procedure used in breast cancer patients to determine if the cancer cells have somewhat *behaved* and contained their party to the breast tissue or if they have been traveling outside of the breast. This procedure allows really smart doctor people to get a glimpse at the lymph nodes, one of the first areas that breast cancer can travel outside of the breast on its way to party throughout the body.

This would be the first time since having my wisdom teeth removed my sophomore year in college that I would be put into the land down under. Like legit anesthesia going to sleepy town *under*. It would also be an opportunity for a port to be surgically placed in my arm.

Oh, yes. My arm. If you have any familiarity with cancer you may be thinking, "Girl. You crazy. A port goes in your chest." If you only know about breast cancer because of October, you may think the arm thing is totally normal.

My surgical oncologist told me that most commonly, it is placed in the chest. She also told me that she'd realized that patients shouldn't have to carry yet another scar so prominently after cancer and she asked how I felt about having it in my arm instead. She added, "I don't want you to be 60 and wearing a strapless dress and worried about some scar."

This woman seems to "get" cancer and also seems to get women, I decided. So I went with the arm placement. Of note, this was the same doctor who told me after I asked if I was going to die from this diagnosis, "Girl. We are going to kick the shit out of this cancer." I knew almost immediately that this genius was my type of gal.

So. Back to the sentinel node biopsy. It would be the first of many times I'd be taken back for surgery over the next year of my life. Having only been put under one other time, I was uneasy.

But I got to have my person, Adam, with me. Well, mostly. I got to have him with me until they rolled me away.

We made small talk that morning as I was hooked up to IVs. We laughed. Took a selfie for posterity's sake. We chatted it up with my nurse. I tried to figure out how I could afford a blanket warmer at home. We passed the time from me trading my street clothes for a hospital gown.

Then it was time for me to be rolled away.

I had actually been rolled away from him before. The time that we were at another hospital after we'd found out earlier that our 32-weeker needed to evacuate my uterus. I'd been uneasy that time, too, to be separated from Adam. But I knew I'd see him in the OR. I knew he'd be at my eye-level as the OB and a team of skilled baby deliverers took our third baby from belly to born.

But this time he wouldn't be in there with me and I wouldn't be awake to make jokes. Instead, I would count from ten and go to sleep and wake up, only after the procedure was completely complete.

And so I had my person to get me to that point.

It was the first of many times that I realized how important it was that I'd come into this point in my life already equipped with my Roll Away Person. I believe some people might call this your lobster. Or your Ride or Die.

A Roll Away Person is the one who will sit there with you, being the strong one while your nerves are tweaked as all get out. The person who will hug you or kiss your forehead and tell you that they will see you on the flipside, assuring you that this will all go as planned and they will be there to hug you again, ask you how your nap was, and take video of anything ridiculous or viral sensation-worthy that you might do or say as you come out of anesthesia.

Your Roll Away Person is your numero uno. Your caregiver. The person who shoulders as much of your fight as you, but who also has to watch you go through it. The person who gets way less help and care as they care for you.

A Roll Away Person is the person who is with you as you roll away into an unknown.

We all need a Roll Away Person. It can be your dad or your sister or your spouse. It could even be some person you met on the Internet in a support group or on Tinder. It doesn't matter *who* it is. It matters *how* they are with you. And for you.

72

Everyone needs that person who is going to get how you want to handle those last hours and minutes before something that is as vulnerable as being wheeled away and taken into the care of strangers while you're asleep. For me, my husband, my Roll Away Man, he knows that I always make jokes, and then right before I get rolled out, we make out like teenagers on a hot summer night, say a prayer together, and I say, "Peace out. See you soon."

Sure, it's completely possible to do that part on your own. It's completely acceptable and normal to handle that shit by yourself. But for me, I didn't want to. Because every time I was rolled away, whether for a routine reconstruction or an 8-hour bilateral mastectomy, I wanted those last moments to be spent in a place of happy. I never knew what would come afterward. But I knew in that moment that I could be content with my Roll Away Person. I could find comfort in knowing that we had those times together and that no matter what occurred in surgery, we would always have pre-op.

Find yourself a Roll Away Person. Know that person will always be there beside you until the last minute before you have to move forward and that they will watch until you are no longer able to be seen in view.

And they will be the face that you ask for after you come to. The person who will come in, smiling at you, even when you look like a complete and utter shitastrophe post-surgery. They will get your favorite stocking cap and keep your head warm. They will text all the people you ask them to, sharing updates. They will sit there and hold your hand and tell you that you did great even though you both know that all you actually did was lay there, lifeless and hopped up on drugs while the doctors did their thang.

Find your Roll Away Person. Keep them close. Every time you get to wake up and see their face, be grateful for another chance to love them for being the person you need them to be. And forever and always remember to be that person for them, in return.

LESSON:

Do What You Know How to Do

My friend just had a baby...
My neighbor's dog just had to be put down...
Her dad just had a heart attack...
Their child is in the hospital for mental illness...
He is totally slammed at work and seems really stressed...
She was just diagnosed with _____....
What can I do for them? What would be helpful?

In my years of writing and sharing, I have received countless messages from readers. Funny ones. Sad ones. Mamas who are worried about a spitty babe. Husbands who are concerned for their wife's postpartum. Mothers-in-law who are curious about how to get along with their daughters-in-law. Twenty-two-year-olds who are awaiting a biopsy. Best friends whose friends are awaiting test results. Women who can't figure out why their 3-year-old won't poop on the potty. Strangers who are wondering about the choice I made to keep my nipples. As you can see, the range of topics is wiiiiiiide.

But the most common, the most asked is definitely, "What can I do for them? What would be helpful? What are the best offerings I can make?"

There is something quite beautiful about having had the opportunity to see the good people of the Universe doing their best to be the goodness for others. It has convinced me that the potential we each contain within us to make a difference outside of us, is astounding.

Whether it's a woman who is curious about helping out a friend with a baby in the NICU, a husband trying to understand how to support his wife through an infant loss, a person who wants to know how to truly lighten the load for a family who just received a health diagnosis or has gone through surgery, people want to know the silver bullet solution to be *there* for their person.

Because doing something for someone helps us show them we care. And also, I think that oftentimes, doing something makes us feel like we are doing *something*.

So what *is* that *something*? What is the best thing to do for someone who is going through a time or a thing?

My advice is this: **Do what you know how to do.**

When I got sick, people started asking what was helpful. What would be useful? What would be necessary?

Honestly, I didn't know. And I couldn't think through it all. I was overwhelmed by a *word*. How could I take on the concept of living day to day with that word in my body and life? In the meantime, the army assembled. They started doing things. All the things.

There were t-shirts printed that read *Ashli's Army*. When I first saw them, of course, I cried. As a sorority girl, I will forever appreciate the community that can be achieved from a t-shirt. Some wore them as they walked in a local event. Others wore them on a Tuesday. And every time I received a snapshot of someone telling me they were wearing theirs, it made me smile.

My carpool partner set up a meal train. For six months. SIX MONTHS. She said she knew that people always offer to help right at the beginning of someone's hard, but then sometimes you get a month down the road and all resources have been exhausted. So she managed the Sign Up Genius for months. And the train kept on making sure we were fed.

Could we have put together our own meals? I would guess so. After all, Adam and I had long been meal planning people. BUT. People stepping in, putting meals in our mouths, and lessening our load was incredible. There were so many days I would shuffle down to the fridge, eyes barely able to open, and feel relief when, magically, there was food to nourish my need for calories.

The army was extensive and well-prepared to take on the battle. And because I want to fully explain and paint a picture of what *do what you know how to do* means, you are about to read through a long list of people and things. Not because this is my Oscar acceptance speech. But because if you are standing by and don't know what to do, I hope this will show you just how deep and wide the net can be cast.

The meal train. As I noted, friends signed up and brought meals. And not just a casserole. We are talking *meals* of a main dish, fruit, veggies, side dishes, desserts, treats for the kids. The controller of the train, Carpool Mom, asked me for a list of *likes, dislikes, allergies, and aversions*. When I got to the point where my boys staged a revolt against red-sauced food, she updated the parameters. When my taste buds were fried from chemo and I could only eat the blandest of the bland foods, Carpool Mom put the kibosh on spice. She handled it for me.

As a mom, I would not have *asked* anyone to assume my role as the meal manager. I most definitely would have just muddled through, not wanting to burden anyone else. But having it done for me was priceless. And allowed me to use any energy I had and put it to the boys and my health.

One of the first friends to bring a meal brought a massive pile of paper plates. She told me that the last thing I needed to worry about was a sink of dishes. This. Was. Ingenious. Yes, I know that some of you are going to slam the book right now and scream about killing the environment, but honestly, I don't mind if you are mad that we used paper plates for almost six months straight.

And that I often even acknowledged that we were possibly killing the environment while killing cancer. The plates meant we could, as we always had, sit down to a meal each night, and know that the cleaning up would be less daunting without scrubbing dishes.

Some of our very closest couple friends own their own business. They asked one of their devoted employees if, one day a week she would mind spending a morning at our house going through mail, picking up around the house, and running errands. I never ever would have thought to ask for *that* kind of help. I never ever would have had the balls to ask. But when they offered, we said, "Sure." And it was both generous and extremely sanity-preserving.

Friends would pop over in the mornings or afternoons as I was awaiting all of my information in the first three weeks. They would sit in my living room as I would cry to myself until I was so exhausted I'd finally fall asleep. They sat as I slept because they knew that in that moment of my life, I was always so afraid of waking up alone. In the days where I wanted to laugh, they laughed with me. And on the days that I wanted to sit in silence, they understood. The presence of people, the reminder that I did not *have* to be alone, provided comfort.

A group of Phi Mu sorority sisters took a donation pool and sent it into the Breast Cancer Research Foundation. They knew that the future of my disease and the research that was to come was valuable to my life. That was a thoughtful use of their resources. One sold necklaces to raise money for another charity. And so many sent constant encouragement.

More people than I'd ever known were in my corner dropped off care packages, including bracelets and t-shirts and blankets. Wonder Woman branded items. Fuck Cancer paraphernalia (literally. Look up the company). Pink item after pink item. And I will say that *pink* can be polarizing. But, for me, the shirts and the jewelry, stocking caps, socks, sweatshirts, and on and on became my *armor*. I wore those gifted items to chemo and felt covered by their thoughts and prayers.

Friends from my hometown sent flowers, notes, and texts. They reached out to say they were praying. The woman who had maintained my hair throughout my youth, and was also battling breast cancer, drove up to hand-deliver a custom blanket. The woman who coached me on the volleyball court and is also a survivor, passed along her copy of *Silver Linings.* One friend took photos. Classmates wore tshirts for myself and another classmate who has her own battle. A woman sent stuffed frogs. And my best friend from Middle School, now a pediatrician, sent the most hilarious stuffed *tumor, c diff, and strep throat* – a reminder that the two of us will always have humor.

Mail arrived from as far as Canada, Japan, and The Netherlands. Regular deliveries from the East Coast. West Coast. Arizona. Texas. Michigan. Minnesota. And on and on.

My uncle sent me a card. Every week. Like clockwork. A funny card. A note about his life that week. Small talk, really. But it was big, to me.

A friend picked up alllll of my Christmas gifts and wrapped them. And then returned them, beautifully ready for a magical Christmas season for my boys. The biggest gift was her time.

A friend who had known me since childhood sent a "box of sunshine." All yellow items. All bright and cheerful. Her mom sent the boys mail. With $2 bills inside.

The boys loved those three or six $2 bills. It was a novelty to them. And I loved the $2 bill because no one really knew but two has always felt lucky to this girl who was born into the world on 2/22/82. The small gesture of a card and a few $2 bills made a big imprint in my journey.

Having just moved into our home about a month prior to treatment, many of our belongings were still in boxes. One friend offered her interior design brilliance and installed a gallery wall. The place that felt like a house started to feel more like a home.

One friend, who I'd eventually begin calling my guardian angel, offered to be a no-questions-asked drop off for my boys whenever there was a need. Last minute IV fluids required, a therapy appointment, desperate need of no germs around my weakened immune system? She was my go-to. Others were on speed dial and would, at a moment's notice, take our boys. For a 6, 4, and 2-year-old to be welcome into so many hearts gave my mama heart quite the tug.

Barrett and Jonah's teachers watched out for them at school and provided safe, comforting environments. And Barrett's school counselor and Principal helped me by checking up on him and giving him an outlet to share any feelings he was having.

My godmother, a longtime framily member, sorority sisters, my mother-in-law, Harrison's godmother, and a few others became my Crashli Crew. They were the people who were present in my house when inevitably, three days post-chemo, I could not even open my eyelids because the exhaustion was all-consuming. That crew provided kid coverage during the days on and after surgeries, driving me to appointments, helping around the house, and keeping life fun and pseudo-normal for the boys. They allowed me to cry alone in my room and then pulled me out of the funk by providing human interaction. They allowed Adam to continue working and having *some* semblance of normal in life.

Adam's employer was patient and generous. They put together huge gift baskets for each of us. They included bags for the kids to open every month while I was going through treatment with holiday activities for each corresponding month and hundreds of dollars of cash and gift cards to help fill some gaps. A supportive employer made things easier.

A cousin offered us all of his sign-in info for his streaming services. He noted that while he didn't have a lot to offer, he knew that people have to lie around a lot throughout the months of treatment and may spend time in the hospital. HBO. Netflix. Showtime, and the like. Knowing I had unfettered access to Sex and The City reruns often made my day.

My parents and my husband's parents took turns manning weekdays and weekends whenever it was possible. They allowed me to have rest and to heal as I was going through treatment so

I'd be able to enjoy moments with the boys and Adam when-ever possible. My sister and sisters-in-law came to my rescue time and time again. My brother's phone calls calmed me. My nephews and niece all brought me hugs and smiles. And our extended families extended their reach by providing prayers and positive thoughts.

My family, those by blood and those through life, were all-in whenever and however they could be, leaving me grateful and humbled, day after day.

The mail. The MAIL. Books. Cards. Quilts. Scripture-filled writ-ings. Flowers. Sticky notes. Hand drawn arts and crafted cre-ations from friends' kids. Key chains. Gift cards. Thoughtful trinkets and inspirational tchotchkes. Holiday attire. Earrings. Scarves. Oils. Head bands. Hats. Leggings. Mugs. Notepads. Items with healing properties. Shakes. Groceries. One of my favorite things: a pomegranate. Yes. A fresh, real pomegranate accompanying a gift certificate for acupuncture. Funny mugs for tea. Kolaches for the freezer. Wine for the bar. iTunes gift cards for music and apps. DVDs to watch. Candles. Markers. Pens. Wall décor. And so much more.

And then very practical offerings (though some might include wine in this list, as well), including herbal teas. Skin care. Lo-tions. Biotene dry mouth rinse. Lip balm. Post-mastectomy pil-lows. Epsom salt for tub soaking. Lemon drops and butterscotch discs. Water bottles to always have at reach. Warm socks for chemo. Prayer shawls for comfort. Baking soda for mouth rins-ing. And every three weeks, a container of Matzo Ball soup from my friend appeared in my fridge for post-chemo consumption and boxes of Tea Smith Tea showed up on my front porch.

The mail and drop-offs came in a steady stream and so often left my mouth agape, wondering if I'd ever been as kind and thought-ful to people as they were being to our family.

Texts and voicemails from family and friends to let me know that they just prayed for me. Or that they saw something hilarious. Or checking in on how I was handling things. Short and long con-versations, including laughter and tears. People listened when

I needed to talk and talked when I just needed to listen. Some gifted their time, popping over to make a dinner, tend to a task around the house, clean up after the kids, take the boys to a pumpkin patch, or just be present for a bit and provide some company. Others traveled distances to be able to give me a hug or clean my floor.

When I mentioned that I wanted to make the boys' Christmas magical, people who have become like a second set of parents to me, constructed a built-in for us, lifted it into the house through a second-story window, and then installed it in the playroom. They stayed the weekend, playing chubby bunny, cleaning the house, and making memories that I will have for a lifetime.

People took on the duty of "Driving Miss Lazy"—what I called it when people had to drive me around post-surgeries when I was on the heavy hitting pain meds. Others took to making sure the boys made it to and from school and pre-k. Family and friends snuggled my boys when my counts had taken a dive.

Friends sat with me at chemo. Others delivered cupcakes from a thousand miles away. A friend offered her expertise in handling anxiety. Another would drop iced tea off on my doorstep. My neighbor, a high schooler at the time, came over to apply false eyelashes when, my lashless lids were heading out to an event. One gave me skincare because her job as an esthetician meant that what she knew was skin. Another friend snapped photos of our family before I lost my hair. A moment in time that I so needed captured with my boys. And when a woman donated the gift of a henna crown for my hairless dome, pictures were taken, once again.

One of my besties gave me a ticket for me to go with her to see Taylor Swift in concert. Another took it upon herself to give me pot for if/when the pain became too much to handle. A nurse who worked with my mom made herself available to me at all hours of the day when I was decimated by anxiety. Nurses offered jokes and remedies for pain and aches. Friends sent lash serum for the day that a new set would start to grow. I received Devotionals to turn to in moments of worry. And sheet music as a reminder to pick up my guitar when days felt so far from normal.

I received crosses to cling to. Evil Eyes to ward off negative energy. And some of the best variations of crispy rice treats that otherwise, I'd never have known existed. A book of quotes collected from friends that I took in my chemo bag and flipped through as a reminder of my army. Bracelets with scripture and bracelets with profanity. Soft pajamas for lazy days, socks for chemo days, and lipgloss for the days where I felt well.

People going through treatment at the same time as me became those I could commiserate with. People who had been there, done that, and had been surviving and thriving since reached out to let me know there would be horrible days but always, silver linings. People who had experienced their very own loss and grief lined up to help me through mine. There were days and weeks that were bad and ugly, and yet, sprinkled with good.

The community that had grown with Baby on the Brehm helped me as I looked for ways to spread goodness through what I called Giftaways and Goodness projects. Business owners and companies provided products and experiences with no strings attached and allowed me to brighten someone's day in the way that so many of mine were being brightened. The people that social media calls *followers* were not following me, they were walking beside me through treatment. A community, some who were once strangers on the Internet became meaningful to me. An actual character in my story. People whose prayers and vibes made an incredible impact on my healing and my ability to cope.

From high school friends to friends I just met, college acquaintances to people I'd worked with, my church family, my actual family, and my life-earned family, everyone seemed to be doing, for me, what they knew how to do.

I know there was more. I'm sure I'm leaving out a ton. But if I added every single thing in, this book would be never ending. Because truly, everything was being thought of by people who weren't me. Adam manned the house and the boys and me with every bit of himself. And everyone else lined up right with him.

We had an army. I don't know *why* we received that blessing, but I've decided to not try to figure out the why and instead, be so grateful for it.

Not everyone has an army. I know this.

So. What can you do to help someone going through something? You can take any of the ideas I've shared here, and make them your own. Or, you can do what you know how to do. If someone is dealing with a personal shitstorm and you feel compelled to do something for them, my suggestion is that you go with the Nike philosophy and *just do it*. You may be the only one who does.

Through letting people in, I was able to let go. I was able to rest. I was able to heal and make cancer and fighting it with treatment and surgeries and as much gusto as I could give, a priority.

Because of all of the individuals in our world doing what they knew how to do, I was able to fight and heal. And in the end, those were the things I needed most of all.

LESSON:

There Will Always Be Laundry. If We're Lucky. (Part 1)

*Y*ah. Perspective. I sorta hate perspective. It's the worst. Because there you are, trying to have your own little (or huge raging) pity party and BOOM. Perspective shoves its way onto your guest list. For a long while, I closed the door on perspective, because I didn't need that kind of guilt in my life. *Go away, perspective.*

When my boys were teensy tinytons, I was tired. Scratch that. I was in a state of walking hibernation. I was running on complete autopilot. Roaming in the dark to get a baby nourished. Truly losing track of the day. The night. The feedings. The poopings. Of the babes. Of my own. I felt...lonely.

But how? How could I feel lonely when I had a constant companion? How could I feel lonely when I was never *alone*? How could I have lost the person I had been for the first quarter of my life in the first month of his?

Because motherhood.

Because I was in a new universe. Unknown territory. A place unfamiliar to every part of my had-gone-to-college-for-a-degree-to-do-all-the-things-and-take-over-the-world self. I was, in some ways, on an island in the middle of the ocean with no understanding of the tide. I was attached to a little human that God had entrusted in my care. And yet, detached from so many other parts of my identity. I felt a little Tom Hanks in Castaway—on my island, talking to this screaming little baby like he was my volleyball, my Wilson, the only person with me in this place that we were in.

I know. That paragraph got a bit dramatic. But truly. Wilson. Errrr, in my case, Barrett. We were in it together every day, all day. We were the two who were figuring each other out. And while I knew that certainly other humans had been raising humans for all of human existence, weeeeeeellll...I felt like I certainly had to be the first that felt this way. Because all the other mamas seemed happy.

And I seemed covered in smog.

I wasn't unhappy. I mean, I guess maybe I was. I did cry a lot of days. But I felt like my basic needs had been replaced with my heart's need to quell my baby's cries. Eating, sleeping, pooping—it felt like there was only time and energy for one of us to do those things. I felt it my maternal duty to make sure that if only one of us could have our needs met, it needed to be him. Or someone would surely call CPS on me.

It was a time. It was a truly *hard* hard.

But then after having babies—two years after the last one was placed in my arms and I rejoiced and praised God that he arrived safely even though I knew that the time ahead of us, the time in the NICU and the time growing him at home would be *hard*— then I found out I had cancer and I thought, *Oh my goodness, I rode the struggle bus through the infant stage, how on earth am I going to do cancer?!*

I did it. And indeed, it was hard. But cancer didn't make that challenging baby stuff any easier.

I still contend that it was my hardest hard. Three times over, three premature infants, three who screamed and cried and spit-up and were inconsolable. It was my hard.

Because *that* is what I realized later. That hard was too hard for perspective to push through the cracks of my broken moments.

I coined some words: Perspective is only good in retrospect.

I know, I sound jaded.

When we are going through something hard, it does not matter one stinking morsel *what* our hard is. Hard is hard because of how it feels to us. How it strikes us in our bones. Not how someone else defines the idea of hard. So when we are going through something hard, you know what often doesn't help? Perspective from jolly happy shinies.

When my toddler is having a fit in Target and another mom says, "Oh. Don't stress. Those days are gone in a flash. You'll want them back sooner than soon." Ummmm. Mmmm k, *Target Mom,* I am not where you are right now. My kid is throwing a conniption-fit over the fact that I put the Mickey Mouse undies in the foldy basket and not in the big basket even though he asked me to put it in the foldy basket. So no. I do not need the guilt from you of feeling like the past 43 seconds of his wails will be one of my most-loved moments of motherhood.

Perhaps I will agree, later that night, as I sip on a four-dollar-screwtop bottle of adult grape juice from Trader Joe's and I look back on the day. Perhaps it'll sink in as I watch my child finally close their eyes and rock, silently. Perhaps I'll have this epiphany as I know that I did the very hardest of my hard. *That* is when perspective really shines for me. That is when I can sit for a moment and feel thankful for things like a warm house, a healthy baby, a free season of Housewives, or even endless laundry, because it means that I am blessed with enough clothes to have dirty clothes. It is in retrospect...hindsight...it is when the moment is past that I am able to understand what the hard was for.

But in the moment, sometimes I just don't need the guilt of feeling awful about myself for being ungrateful and wishing my crying baby would just give me a reprieve. For just a moment. So I don't feel so incapable of mothering. Nurturing. And humaning.

Check the gas gauge. Know that you can't fill the tank in a mere moment's time. Before you offer perspective to someone, take the temperature of the environment and know that your warm fuzzies will not unfreeze the frozen tundra at a moment's notice.

The truth from the time of newly-minted-motherhood for me is that I *was* alone in that. *I* was the only one who was mothering our first-born. I was the one who was getting to know him, daily.

I was exhausted. My hormones were trashed. My nipples were bruised, battered, and confused by the fact that while they had previously been used for sexual arousal, they were now able to feed a person. My hair was falling out and breaking and shedding the layer of shimmer it had owned during pregnancy. My downtown lady parts were more torn up than wrapping paper on Christmas morn. It was a time.

A hard time.

The day I was told I should get a mammogram was a mindscrew of epic proportions. I was scared. I was not in control. I was whacked out of my gourd. Looking back...it is still hard. It remains hard. It did not become easier. And I do not want to ever go through it again.

I think it is essential that we always remember that we do not need to find perspective in the times that are truly hard. Sometimes, it is just that we need to get through it. And that's all we can do.

87

So I believe that we don't need to be thankful for what having laundry means every time we see a pile. Sometimes, we can begrudge the laundry. We can grumble about the fact that it seems endless. And while that doesn't mean we don't have a clue that we're lucky, it *does* mean that we don't have to like it.

Sometimes the hard parts are hard and looking at it through someone else's rose-colored-glasses just seems to make it harder. So perspective-shmermective. Let the good moments feel good, and let the bad moments feel heavy. Because that's how we flex our muscles in the end, anyway.

LESSON:
Life Includes Suffering

There was a prickly, stinging that rushed from beneath my skin. My chin quivered. Tears began to stream down my face. I sat there sobbing as a friend said, "She probably only has days left."

Days.

Not years. Not decades. Not happily ever after. No. *Days.*

She had received her diagnosis before me. Her breast cancer was metastatic. Stage 4. An advanced breast cancer diagnosis with a less-flowery prognosis than my stage 2. A diagnosis that still has no silver bullet to halt progression.

When my diagnosis came, so did her name. Everyone asked if I knew Jennifer. She was also a young mother of three young children. As my months of treatment went on and I heard her name again and again, I realized I had met her on my first day of chemo. And then it occurred to me that we'd known each other in a former life before either of us ever knew cancer.

And then. I sat in Bible Study having been declared free of cancer, only to hear that she was dying from it.

Days.

I felt bad for not knowing it had progressed so far. I felt bad for not reaching out. For being so out of the loop. I felt bad. And sad.

And of course, I questioned *why.*

Why did Jennifer's cancer have to be so shitty? Why was she having to kiss her children goodbye? Why would her husband, Kyle, have to move forward on earth without his wife? When suffering and pain are the hand someone is dealt, I wonder *why.*

It shouldn't come as a surprise, right? It's no different than anything else in life. People are born. People live. People *die.* But it's not that simple, is it? Because those people who are born and who are living, they touch us. They have friends. And family. Sometimes, they have babies. They work with colleagues. They belong to clubs. So it's not as black and white as *we arrive and then we go.* We are not just simply put here to *live.* We are often here long enough connect. Perhaps to know love. To, many times, *become.* We are life-full. We are full of moments. Breaths. Life.

We do not merely appear and then die. We live. And the more we live, the harder it is to believe that we don't always get to have eternal *earthly* life. The longer we live, the more we grow attached to the people we meet. The more they grow attached to us.

I find the more I am attached to life, the more I have questions about suffering and death. Hundreds of times, I've asked *why.*

Why has my sister's father-in-law, Rich, been diagnosed with cancer again and again?

Why did Jennifer have to leave Wendi and the rest of her family so soon?

Why were Kala and Cynthia and so many others dealt a metastatic diagnosis?

Why did Johnny and Lori only get to know their baby, Ethan for hours instead of years?

Why have mothers around me had to bury their tiny children before they even got to grow up?

Why did my classmate, Brian, get hit by a train when he was just trying to haul grain? Or my friend Abe's aunt have to suffer the same fate when her car crossed the tracks?

Why did my dad and his siblings have to say goodbye to my grandpa Don so prematurely?

Why did my cousin Travis die so suddenly when he'd worked so hard to get back to his life?

Why did Greyson, such a happy little boy, have to battle Spinal Muscular Atrophy?

Why did Pamela have to lose her daughter and then watch her husband lose his battle?

Why did Stacey lose two of her three triplets?

Why did my teacher, Mrs. Marks, with her radiant smile, have to go through so much pain?

Why did Julie's kids have to lose their mother and then, months later, have their father, Justin, diagnosed with cancer?

Why did Jennifer only have days left in her life? Why didn't she get to continue to be life-full? Why didn't her drugs work? Why did her kids have to say goodbye?

I know. This is going to happen. People are going to have cancer. Having had cancer, I am going to continue to meet people with different stories than mine. But because we are all categorized under one term — Cancer — it somehow feels even more unfair to me now.

Having felt the suffering of postpartum blues, body image struggles, loss of a pregnancy, and paralyzing anxiety, I find that my heart hurts more for others battling their own hard parts of life. Our own suffering seems to develop our ability to empathize. Our own pain seems to develop our ability to want others to heal.

Is that why there is suffering in life? Do we have to know suffering to know joy? Do we have to feel pain to know the feeling of healing? Do we have to know death in order to appreciate life?

I do not know the answer.

I know that Jesus suffered. I think as a Christian, that is supposed to make me feel better about the existence of suffering. But it doesn't. I want it to. Yet even in knowing that Jesus suffered on the cross and did so for our sins, as a woman in this modern world, suffering still feels unfair.

I know that for centuries, people have endured hardships. I think as a human, that is supposed to help me understand that they are just a part of life. But it doesn't. Hardships still feel heavy and burdened.

I know that no one makes it out of this life alive. I think as a living, breathing soul, this is supposed to make the losing and the ending seem normal. But it doesn't.

I don't know why some people experience more pain than seems possible.
I don't know why some get better and some don't.
I don't know why there is disease, poverty, or anguish.
I don't know why some people are born into fortunate circumstances and others are born into chaos.
I don't know why some get fired, why others have to battle depression, why people suffer abuse, why some experience horrible marriages or awful teenagers.

The suffering still doesn't make sense to me.

I cried that day as Jennifer was dying. I cried when I received a message that she passed. I was sad that she had to go. And yet, in her ending, I was so thankful she no longer had to suffer.

I hugged my boys extra tight that night. Who am I kidding? I've hugged them extra tight every night since I got cancer. I think of Jennifer often. I think of Julie, Lori, Travis, Greyson, Abigail, Parker, and so many more.

I know that life includes suffering.

I also know that in all the suffering, there always seem to be glimpses of goodness. Examples of the deep down goodness of the human spirit. Realities that can renew our faith in humanity. And filled with gratitude for the beauty of it all, even amongst the rubble.

It is an absolute truth that if we spend any amount of time taking breaths on this earth, we will feel, we will love, we will suffer, and we may even keep going. Through suffering and sadness, joy and goodness, and asking a million *whys* life goes on until it doesn't.

LESSON:

There Will Always Be Laundry. If We're Lucky. (Part 2)

So, the baby thing for me was hard. For others, the first part of being a mom is the happiest and loveliest and skipping-in-daisiest time of their lives. And that is wonderful.

Truly.

I don't say that with one single ounce of sarcasm or angst. We are, each and every one of us, different, and *that* is a true gift of the universe, isn't it? Because we each have our gifts, our strengths, our likes and dislikes. We each have the most wonderful privilege of becoming undone from the start and of figuring out what life looks like from our own view.

I know I said that I'm sorta over perspective, but adversely, I believe that it is also quite capable of putting our lives in order. Because here's the thing about life and humans...both are always changing, growing, and learning. There are times where we need to say "take your perspective and shove it, please" (because please makes that kind).

Times where I personally have found perspective to be *shit* include the following:

> One of my friends was going through a marital shitstorm about a decade ago. It was awful. The outlook was bleak. The darkness was covering her visibility. Her life was, at that time, crumbling. It was awful. And no amount of people telling her their stories or stories of other people's misfortune could alleviate her pain. It was *her* pain she was feeling. Not theirs. Perspective did not deserve a seat at her table.

> Another friend had a child who had to have surgery. The surgery went awry. Then there was another surgery. Annoyances and other crap rained down on them for months. Then suddenly their second child had the same needs. It was a hard time. And it just *had* to be hard.

Maybe you've been there. Maybe you've been on the road that is winding and it feels like you are going to fly off the rails. Maybe you are there right now. And here's the thing. You still have to get through this. You do. We can't go over it. We can't go under. We have to go through.

Which might suck.

But that's not because you are weak or a bad person or anything resembling an angry troll who set up shop under a bridge. No. You are human.

Good news though. Sometimes perspective is the perfect light for our dark dark day.

Then one day that fog, or that smog, those dirty, heavy clouds that are looming overhead will begin to dissipate *just enough*. And then. *Ahhhhhhhhhh. Then. Then.*

Grab that perspective. Hold tight. It will tug at you, the other side of the rope. It will try to pull you back into the muck. THEN.

Focus on the perspective. Start making a daily gratitude list. Heck, start making a list every other day, adding one thing you are thankful for that isn't pulling your world into the deep hole of shit. Start thinking about the laundry.

But only then. Only when the perspective doesn't cover you in guilt. I do not believe you need to say, "I cannot be stressed by work because that person just lost their husband." Yes. A person losing their spouse is horrible. It is heart wrenching. It is *hard*, I am almost sure. But it is not in the baggage you are carrying. It isn't the same type of hard as your work situation. But it is still hard.

So when you are in a place where the perspective will not weigh you down even more or make you feel empty for feeling sorry for yourself, then and only then, think about the laundry. Look at yourself in the mirror and say, "I'm so thankful that I got to get out of bed today," or "I am so in love with those two minutes where my baby smiled yesterday," or "I am so thankful for the health of my child." Because only once the light shines in a bit will you see the glimmer in the laundry.

Perspective can be a useful tool in battling our hard. It can be a coping mechanism used to make our heavy loads feel carryable. It can help us know what a gift it might be to have dirty laundry every day because it means we have more than enough.

But please, don't let someone in Target make you feel like you are getting it wrong. Don't let someone who has never done your hard tell you that it isn't as hard as theirs. And do not, do not, *do not* weigh your life against another's unless it is to help you heal, cope, and function. Otherwise, just wait for the glimmer. Or the moment where your feet touch the floor and you feel the light for a moment. Then, write it down, and carry the note with you all day.

Yes, we are fortunate to have laundry. It means that we have an overabundance. But when it feels forever like dirty laundry, when it feels as if your load is sullied and hampered, don't be afraid to throw up your hands, and go, "This is hard. And I have to get through it. I have to survive it. Then, I will figure out how to thrive." And then when the light shines in, you will feel like you can hold on tight and maybe even enjoy the cries, the unknown, and the ride.

LESSON:

There's Beauty in the Beneath

*D*ay 13. That's what they told me as I was snuggled under a warm blanket, reclined in the chemo chair. *About* Day 13, your hair will begin to shed. It sounded so odd, and though I'd seen other people go through cancer and lose their hair, it was hard to imagine that in about two weeks, my mid-length blonde locks would begin to fall.

I decided I would take matters into my own hands. I set up an appointment with my hair stylist, a woman who'd become a friend. A woman who'd known my hair through thick and thin as I'd seen her over the last five years. I asked her for a preemptive pixie.

She cut. And cut again. She asked as she cut each "level" if it was too short. I relayed that it was easier for me to know I was taking control of the situation. It helped me to know I wouldn't be shedding long blonde hairs all over the house. She was helping me begin the grieving process.

On Day 13, I ran my hand through my pixie style. I expected to feel a tugging of the hair being removed from the follicles. When I didn't, I decided that it must not be the day it would begin to make its exit. Until I looked at my hand. Day 13, and hair coated my hand. There was no feeling of it coming out. It just was. Each time I brushed or swept my hand through, there was less hair on my head. My head began to tingle and itch. I decided it was time. I didn't want to pull out hair in front of my boys. I wanted to maintain some delusion of control. So we scheduled our party.

On a Friday night, with Adam, my boys, my in-laws, Lyle and Kathy, and Adam's sister, Kim, in on the fun, I sat on a stool in my kitchen. With a garbage bag covering my shoulders, I held a shot of tequila in one hand, and a cross in the other. I laughed and swore and toasted and my husband and my Middlest shaved my head. At age 33, for the first time since I was an infant, I was bald.

I looked at wigs. I even grabbed a couple from a free wig bank at my treatment center. But I just couldn't find one that felt familiar. My boys preferred my bald dome. I did, too. I fashioned scarves when I ventured out to run errands. Stocking caps for when I was hanging out at home or with friends. I realized that though I would probably always care what people thought of me, it wasn't enough of a care to wear a wig to make someone else feel more comfortable. I think it was one of the first times that I truly cared more about my appearance affording comfort to myself than others.

I felt so *light*. And that feeling had *zero* to do with a scale.

Over the months of chemo, every hair on my body was banished. From my head to my legs. My eyelashes and brows. The hairs in my nose were gone.

What was left was skin and bones. My smile and my spirit. I was stripped down. Eventually, even my breasts would be gone.

It sounds sad. It might even look sad, to see a person who looked like I did, one without so many comforts of our common culture. Vibrant locks. Luscious lashes. Perfectly penned in brows. And yet, I felt *comfortable.*

I felt comfortable in the shell that was left after the rest of the glamour had been stripped away was just *me*. It was somehow freeing.

This was the same body I'd always had. The body I was born with 33 years earlier. The one that had, in so many different stages, worn the swimsuit. The body that I hated in my late teens. The body that I deprived and punished for looking a certain way. Or for *not* being able to fit into a certain size. The body that carried three babies for me. The one that couldn't wait to go balls to the walls of life once again.

In carrying my babies, I started to see the beauty. I started to see the miracle of the human form. The gift of getting to be a vessel for another. I started to understand that my body had always been a rock star even when I'd been making it sing backup for so many stages of my existence.

I was lucky enough to have a sister-in-law, who helped me be grateful for the function that my body offered. The way that I could laugh from my belly. The world I could see through my eyes. The movement I could feel because of my joints and muscles and bones. The holding of children that my hips allowed. And the loving I was able to feel because of my heart.

It was in motherhood that I began to legitimately comprehend self-love and body acceptance. Because I could see that in all its forms, this skin I'd been walking around in supported me—living, breathing, being—through over three decades.

Then came cancer and chemotherapy. And the undoing of all the learned beliefs on beauty and appearance I'd collected from media and our culture. Bald. Not a single hair left on my body. My coloring, sallowed from treatment. But somehow, in my rawest form, I could see beauty. I could see beneath.

It was so simple, really. A chance that not everyone can experience or mimic. To take away the pressure of hair and makeup and exercising for vanity and instead focusing on my health and my happiness was a daily reminder that less is more. That when we feel like there are no exterior expectations of our appearance, our internal contentment with what our bodies can do and how they can survive becomes more of a focus than what it looks like.

When I had no control over my body, I let go of the need to control it. When I had no hair to fix, I found myself less likely to try to *fix* who I was. When I was skin and bones and smile and soul, I can honestly say that it was easier for me to feel my true beauty. That which is in the beneath.

We pile so much on top of ourselves day-in and day-out. We see messages over and over about how we look, how much we weigh, how *strong* we appear, what we *shouldn't* be eating, how to be the "best version of ourselves." And yet the beauty is truly underneath it all.

As my hair began to grow back, it was a chance to be whatever I wanted to become next. I named my hairstyles—my favorite was Blanche—to embrace the experience in order to get to the next.

My weight fluctuated a million times with hormone blockers, medication changes, dietary restrictions, and the life of a woman who has carried three babies. Through it all, it has been my object to focus on eating what fuels me and what fills me. It has become my habit to—unless I am at the doctor's office—stay off the scale. It has become my mantra that my body is amazing. Because an amazing body is so far beyond skin-deep.

And now, I eat dessert when I want dessert. I also eat a lot of green things. I don't label foods with words like "bad" or "cheating" but I do believe in being aware of what I am putting in my body. I believe in taking walks because I like to be outside, not just to hack away at a step count. I think about the way that I am honoring my body for all it has done and prepare it for all I have left to do. And yes, I have cellulite. I don't know if I have abs. But I wear the swimsuit, not to show off my body but to allow it to be in the sun.

Does this mean I'm anti-Botox, facials, or pampering? Um, no. Or that I never wear makeup or get my hair colored? Nope. Does this mean I don't want to keep my body strong or healthy or challenged? Nah. In every bit of honesty, I still assess my physical form. I still take steps to brighten, tighten, and care for this shell of mine. And my body is in progress, just like my life.

But I carry the lessons of the *beneath* with me I have great gratitude for the miracles my body has performed. I am so stunned and in awe of its ability to be torn apart and pieced back together again, with scars left behind to remind me of the roadmap of my trials and triumphs. But the further out I get from those days, the more I can feel those reminders slipping through my grasp. And every so often, when people start bemoaning their weight and labeling foods as "good and bad" I know the world is trying to push its way in once again.

I think it is human nature, in the time we live in with messages of comparison splattered every which where, to be pulled to the dark side of believing that looking different than we once did isn't beautiful. We listen to the whispers that because we are older or have been cracked open, we are not as valuable. We count wrinkles as failures. We call the shifting of our skin a misfortune. We see the evidence of years on this earth as something that requires every bit of fixing we can apply.

When the lessons of cancer start to get pushed around by everyday life. When the existence of the purest form of beauty being buried in our beneath start to slip away or out of the forefront of my mind, I have to close my eyes, open my heart, and say, "my body is amazing." I have to push back in order to remember to be grateful that the beauty lives within me.

I remind myself over and over that our bodies were made to be broken and put back together, in different configurations, over and over again. Just like our old pal Humpty Dumpty.

I look back at photos of my stripped-down state and I see the contentment I had in my own skin. I hold that tight to my soul so it shines right in, rays of realization that I am a beautiful being, that my body is a badass, and that I am just as I was meant to be in this time and place.

We must remind the person who looks back at us in the mirror that they are merely a reflection of what we might be feeling on any given day. We are so much more than what rises to the surface when put under the best angles and light.

Not everyone will have a time where they feel firsthand, the beauty of being bald. Thank goodness. Not everyone has a circumstance that leads them to bare the beneath. But everyone holds the power to push back.

And so every morning, when our eyes open up, once again, we can start by saying, "Thank you for being here again," to our bodies. We can believe that we are given a tremendous opportunity of another day to be beautiful. Beautiful in our actions. In our words. In our being. To be exactly who we know we are beneath it all.

LESSON:

They Are Sisters, Not Twins

*B*oob cancer is weird. I mean, it's also ridiculously awful because, well, it's cancer. But it's also weird. Because boobs are weird.

The makeup of a breast is essentially fat, a little muscle, some ducts, and a nipple. The whole idea of nipples is just bizarre to me. Like boobs without nipples are just any other part of the body, right? But then you adorn these two mounds of fat (or maybe not mounds if your boobs are anything like mine were pre-cancer and post-nursing) with a little nubbin on top and boom—sexy fat, apparently.

It is at this point where I would like to share that pre-cancer and pre-nursing, when my boobs were just young pups, I actually had a business idea of selling fake nipples that you could stick on other parts of your body to make the "fat" more attractive to the human eye. For instance, why wouldn't six nipples on my outer and inner thighs also turn them into sexy fat? It makes two random chest balls "sexy" and all those are is fat and ducts, right? If that's not foreshadowing, I don't know what is. But I digress...

I was never that keen on my rack. I mean, sure, my husband thought it was fantastic (which was very kind of him). But in my estimation, it was nothing to write home about. And I had actually become quite good with that. I kept them mostly under wraps. They kept mostly to themselves, hardly ever allowing for any cleavage to happen because they basically sat as far from one another as possible without chillin' in my pits. So in finding out I had an intruder in the right one, I believe my first thought was, *Good riddance, gals!*

I honestly prefer to call them any word that *isn't* breasts. Because breasts are the evil jerks that tried to kill my joy. So I call them ta tas. Hooters. Tits. Foobs. The girls. Funbags. While I do know that for the general population those words all sound rather crass and would cause either of my grandfathers to roll over in their graves, I personally find it wildly hilarious to assign them as many different monikers as possible since I feel like a cyborg in my chestal region. It's hard to continue calling something by its technical term when technically, you don't have them. And that is why a whole lotta breast cancer survivors call them Foobs (Fake. Boobs.).

Depending on your diagnosis and where your breast cancer situated itself inside the breast cavity, there are options for your process. From a lumpectomy to a radical mastectomy, patients and their doctors are able to discuss what might provide the best outcomes and the least chance of recurrence (not of the breast growing back. Breasts are not worms. But of the cancer growing back.). Each diagnosis and patient are so unique and therefore so are the treatment plans.

Within days of receiving a phone call informing me that much of my right boob was monopolized by pre-cancerous cells, I'd already been made aware that a mastectomy was likely my best option. And once the cancer was confirmed to be invasive, I wanted to get it off my chest and I wanted the boobtender to make mine a double. After chemotherapy and before radiation, just three days after my 34th birthday, I would have a double mastectomy.

For about three seconds, I contemplated no reconstruction at all. I knew of this wildly entertaining comedienne, Tig Notaro, who had gone without reconstruction and began taking her shirt off and performing topless during her comedy act and I thought, *I mean...what if I somehow get a famous comedy gig and I have these huge perky tits? That's way less ironic, right?* But at 33-years-old, it was not really recommended. Apparently studies and research have found that the emotional healing is a smoother process when the survivor has a body somewhat resembling the body they had before the attack on their own soil. After talking with doctors, getting the opinions of survivors, doing a wee bit of googling, and thinking about my husband's one shot at being married to a gal with plump and perky Foobs, I decided that reconstruction would be the route for me.

Almost immediately after the decision was made, boobs were on the brain. Implants. Shapes. Materials. It felt like I was picking out a new car, not a new body part. I found out that while I wanted to be an itty bitty B, the sizing was not exactly up to me but more about the internal cavity and its shape and size. I learned that while there are saline and silicone implants, saline can be left with rippling and dimpling more so than silicone and so they are less likely to be recommended for mastectomy patients. I learned that there are smooth and textured implants and the textured ones are often referred to as "gummy bear implants" due to the way they feel and taste (just kidding. They taste like chicken. Also kidding. I don't know if they have a taste.).

I learned about expanders, pockets that are used as a placeholder and keep the breast cavity open after a mastectomy. The most fascinating nugget I learned about the process of breaking down and rebuilding a breast? I learned that I could keep my nipples.

Yes. I could *keep* my nipples. And I don't mean in a jar on the mantel.

Well, color me surprised! I can keep the weirdest part of a human body? Apparently yes. It's called a nipple-sparing mastectomy (I know. Super creative name.), and not only did my surgical oncologist and other trusted advisers present the option to me...they *recommended* it.

I proceeded forward with the idea to Dr. Johnson and Stacey, both part of my team in Plastic Surgery.

They walked me through it all. Patiently. Thoroughly. The operation. The pain. The healing. The expanders. The filling of the expanders. And eventually, the reconstruction surgery in which they would place the implant.

They explained that breast reconstruction is much different than a *boob job*. That so much of the outcome of the process is dependent on how your skin holds up while being expanded (stretched) and radiated (zapped). And also how your body healed after treatment.

They shared that the scarring would sit under the cup of each breast. That if all went according to plan, my nipples, my God-given nubs, would still be there, centered atop the reconstructed breast. Alternatively, if it didn't, they'd just x-acto knife the little guys right off.

Then Stacey provided the best reminder of all: just remember, they are sisters, not twins.

I know I'd heard that about eyebrows before. That though they seem like they should look alike, they weren't made as carbon copies. And so, of course, were boobs, ears, eyes, elbows, and heck, even labia, I am guessing. Sisters. Not twins.

Sometimes one breast is bigger than the other. Sometimes one nipple is darker. Sometimes one is lower. The outcome after a mastectomy would be no different. There was little chance for perfection. Sisters. Not twins.

I laughed and laughed as we discussed the future of my Foobs. I giggled over the thought of having plump, perky breasts accompanying me through life. I had only one request, "Could I get some cleavage?" The answer, "I think we could manage that."

The plan was set. Bilateral nipple sparing mastectomy with an add-on item of a lymph node dissection (technical term for removal of some or all lymph nodes). Tissue expanders placed, everything sewed back up. Then, over time, I would pop in to my plastic surgeon's office so Stacey could actually stretch the expanders. Then radiation. And six months later, a surgery to place the implant.

I fully understood why I was warned that this was a wee bit more complex than a breast augmentation. I understood that whereas a breast aug was, indeed, painful and intrusive, it was a boob job. A mastectomy, on the other hand, had started to sound like a bona fide boob project.

Three days before my mastectomy, I turned 34. I held a large bash for the people who had helped carry our family through chemo. My *BonBoobvage* included boob cake pops, cupcakes, and booby bevs including Mamma-Ritas and Slippery Nipples. It was the perfect sendoff for my pair. I was ready to bid my original breasts adieu.

I celebrated that night that I'd made it to 34. With so many of the beautiful women I've gotten to know, I celebrated that I'd been blessed with such a wildly weird life. We laughed as we grabbed boobs, positioned cupcakes as boobs, and ate boobs (cupcakes. Not motorboating). For my taste, it was a Mary Poppins type of sendoff, *practically perfect in every single way.*

I cried. I know. That's just shocking. But I figured once again, it was my party and I could cry if I wanted to.

As the day neared for my surgery, I felt ready. I also felt like I was living in some alternate state of reality. Sure, I'd done the whole chemo thing but *this* whole thing felt bizarre. Because boobs are weird. And knowing I was about to be boob-less, even though I'd never liked mine, felt odd.

I took pictures of the "girls" for posterity. I knew from being a human for the last 34 years that my mind would fuzzy over time. I'd forget them. And while I was not pleased with them since they flipped my life on its head, I felt it appropriate to focus on the good times we'd had. The training bra stage (that, for me, lasted about three years). Their maiden voyage in a blue gingham underwired bikini, a yellow daisy placed right in their cavernous divide. My attempts with push-up bras, water bras, Wonderbras, and sticky chicken cutlets to cover and smoosh and support these two ski slopes.

And then there was the nursing. It's a story that is for another book or time but nursing and I were not friends. It took me three babies and three and a half years to finally find joy and contentment in it. But I still felt compelled to thank my mammaries before they were scraped out and thrown to the curb for having helped me feed my boys. For making copious ounces of milk and helping my welterweights thrive.

I didn't know then that those same breasts would teach me how to thrive. How. Weird.

I recalled late nights, rocking one of the boys, their head on my chest, their breathing steady. Steadied by the beat of my heart that rested beneath the tissue and ducts that were soon to be gone. And it was that night, the night before my mastectomy, that I realized how right Stacey was: *They are sisters. Not twins* (and to Debra and Diana, this is not a knock on twins ;-)).

Yes, sisters. Two people who are similar in makeup and background but do not necessarily look alike. Identical twins are two people who have the same genome and are commonly identical at first glance.

In preparing mentally for the whole boob takeover, I appreciated Stacey's analogy. It provided a set of expectations that each breast might have its very own appearance. Sisters. Not [identical] twins.

My sister, Danielle, and I are tight. She is the lefty to my righty. She has always been my person since the day she was willing to chew carrots up before she shoved them in my mouth so, as an infant, I wouldn't choke. Thoughtful, right? Truly, though, she is my best friend. We are similar. But we are also extremely different.

I prefer a conversation. She prefers a book.

The only time I didn't wear mascara was when my eyelashes had fallen out during treatment. The only time my sister wears mascara is when I do her makeup.

Danielle is even keel. I am, well, *everywhere.*

We are different from one another. And while I hoped for my sake that my reconstructed boobs might seem a little bit more similar aesthetically than my sister and I, Stacey's words helped me remember that boobs are not identical.

Sisters, not twins. My body had already been through this. I knew that while bodies are a wonderland of magic, they are constantly in flux. My 13-year-old body in the gingham suit? Vastly different than my college body that didn't want to wear one. My honeymoon body in the white eyelet bikini? Very different than my postpartum form. My body after three babies and my body after chemotherapy? Once again, one of these things was not like the other.

Sisters. Not twins. Our bodies go through a million and two morphings over time and yet we expect them to be twins. We expect our bodies to "go back" or "get back." We look at them in the mirror longing for what they looked like *when* and forget that during *when* we weren't always satisfied with the appearance either. This surgery, while a hugely terrifying life-event for me, would not get to steal my joy of all the things my body had done for me.

I took Stacey's words with me. I reminded myself as I healed: *Sisters, not twins.* When the drains came out and the air was deflated from the expanders (yes, air. I was essentially a walking pumpkin patch jumping pad for a stint of time.) and the fills of fluid began happening, I watched in complete amazement at what had become possible in modern-day breast reconstruction.

When, after I'd received the news that my pathology (technical term for lab results) had shown that there was no cancer left in my breast or my lymph nodes, my right nipple started to resemble a 9-day-old baby's belly button, I told myself, *sisters not twins.*

And when, just shortly after, I started referring to that nipple as the "the bacon bit" and it fell right off, leaving behind its fully-intact counterpart on the left mound, I repeated, *sisters not twins.* I thanked Stacey for having prepared me that it would all come out in the wash, that some things might shrink and others might fair perfectly well.

Since my mastectomy, I've had Phase 2 reconstruction, a procedure where they place the actual implant. And then, about a year later, I had a revision surgery to remove painful scar tissue and upgrade my implants from a teardrop shape to round.

At this point, I am fairly certain that after having accompanied me to 764 doctor's appointments over the last few years, my Littlest thinks I'll take my clothes off for anyone.

For now, I am content with my breasts. I still think they are weird. I have one and a half nipples. And no feeling in any of it because the tissue is gone. They are sisters, not twins. But they are actually the best Foobs I've ever had (also the only, but who's counting). Cleavage? I've got it in spades. Perk? My new set basically starts at my chin. I have even boasted that my left boob is as perfect a breast as I could have ever envisioned and that means I now have one more perfect boob than I ever had before. And because of the way radiation affected Mr. Right Side, I can move the left one up and down in isolation, which, if you ask me, is a pretty impressive party trick.

My body before babies was one thing. My body after babies was, in many ways, different. Different experiences. Different memories. Sisters. My life before cancer, it was lovely. My life post-cancer, it's lovely, too. But they look nothing alike. Same girl. Two different parts of me. Not twins.

Yes, it's weird. Boobs are weird. Nipples are downright bizarre. Twins? Twins are cool. Statistically, they are unique, which seems to make Twinning fascinating to people. The twins who I get to call my friends are indeed fascinating people (and definitely individuals).

Sisters, they're fascinating, too. Similar in their makeup. Generally very different in appearance. But just as fun. And weird. Especially when one has a nipple and the other one only has half.

LESSON:

Just Let Delores Have the Brownie

I am sure you know a *Delores*. And before I go any further, let's all get one thing straight: this actually has nothing to do with anyone who is *actually* named Delores. So, if your name is Delores or your grandmother's middle name is Delores or if your next door neighbor's dog goes by DeDe for short and you're currently wondering if the actual name of said pup is Delores, stop your sweating. This is not about Delores.

What is this about? The person who is a *Delores*. Because if you've ever been through your own challenges (again, WE ALL HAVE/ARE/WILL) you have probably encountered a Delores.

Have you ever watched Notting Hill? You know, the flick with the blue door and Hugh Grant's perfectly coifed hair and Julia Roberts' perfectly perfect everything? The one where they end on the bench? Ohhhhh the bench! That is my favorite. But that is not the point. The point is the brownie.

If you've not seen Notting Hill, do not put this book down. I know in some books, the author would tell you, "Put this book down *right now* and go watch it and come back." But ain't no chance of me telling you to put this book down for fear of you never having time to get back to it. So instead, let me paint the picture for you.

There is a scene in the movie that revolves around *the brownie*. Hugh Grant's character, William, and Julia Roberts' character, Anna, are having dinner with friends of William's. These friends have never met Anna but feel as if they know her and love her because of her fame as an actress. After they eat dinner and dessert, they are enjoying chit chat, and there is just one brownie left. And so, they decide that in order to get that last brownie, they will each share their own personal sob story.

I know. This setup is big. But I promise, it's worth it.

They sit, each sharing their hardships of life. Each vying for the prize of the last brownie to be gifted to the "saddest one at the table."

One shares that his job is shit. That he's gotten fat.

The next, a woman, talks about making no money at her record store job. Notes her bad feather hair. And her shrinking boosies.

Another woman, wheel-chair bound since an accident, shares that she's had to give up her favorite thing—smoking. That she has recently discovered she can't have a baby.

And finally, when they get to Anna, the one who everyone at the table perceives as not having a care in the world or anything sad about her, she shares that she's been on a diet for a decade. She had a boyfriend who hit her. She is constantly crapped on by the media. That although she's had surgeries to fix imperfections, one day...in the not-so-far-future...she will become a has-been in her industry.

Who gets the brownie? Go watch the movie. But not right now, cool? Cool.

Gosh I love this scene so much.

Recently I sat around a table with my family. We celebrated the holidays. And true to our family's tradition, we all took turns saying what we were thankful for. As my turn came, the tears began to well up (of course they did...) and I said, my voice cracking a bit, "I'm just so thankful for everything. To be through it all. It's just been hard. And I'm so happy to be *here*."

My family was quiet for just a moment when my brother smiled and said, "Ash. It's okay. You can have the brownie."

"Ohhhh!!! I don't want the brownie!" I laughed. But I knew and he knew and we all knew that the last few years had changed us all.

I love the brownie scene because it's so applicable in life, right?

Like how many times do we look at someone else, both in life or on the ever-present social media and find ourselves believing that while our life has its twists and turns, other's lives are flawless and perfect?

It's human nature, I think, to compare and to feel like the Anna's have it all. And that they could never have anything brownie-worthy, right? It's so normal to believe that our hard is the only hard of its kind when in reality, once again, *hard is hard is hard.*

I think that most people I come into contact with tend to understand that I don't need for my cancer to be labeled harder than your miscarriage. Your neighbor isn't vying for his bunion surgery to be harder than your insomnia. The girl at the coffee shop is not attempting to make you feel worse for her work schedule than you do for your full calendar.

For the most part, people want to be empathetic to your situation. For the most part, I think people want to validate how others are feeling. To understand that we are all trudging through our own Fire Swamp and that flames can shoot up without warning.

But then, there are the Delores'. I'm guessing you know a Delores. Your secret eye rolls have been all for her. Your conversations after dinner have been about her.

Delores is the one who has always had it harder than you. She is the topper. Or maybe we ought to call her the downer. The one who, no matter what your life has been or how many years you had braces or what your diagnosis was or how long your birth was, well, Delores has had it worse.

Sometimes, when you're sitting in the company of a Delores, you find yourself feeling as if you ought to throw your hat in the ring for that brownie. Because Delores is getting under your collar and you'd really love to get her out.

But guess what? Delores does not even know about the brownie. Delores is not even hearing what anyone else is putting out there. Delores is solely focused on herself. She has no idea that her life revolves around winning the brownie. Delores is the person who, at times, you find yourself wanting to battle and take on with some story about how even though it took her 43 hours to get on her fake eyelashes, it took you 44. Delores is just Delores.

She will, no matter what, wallow in her woes. She will let you know that her cancer was the very worst of any kind of worse that has ever been found. She will be the mom who lets you know that her hard is, in fact, harder than you could ever imagine.

She is the one who cannot and will not find perspective in one ounce of what you are saying. She will never sit amongst the brownie stories and walk away feeling eyes-opened by the conversation. She will not have empathy for the reality that we all feel that our hard parts of life are hard. Instead, Delores will rip that brownie out of your hand and shove it into her mouth while telling you this is the hardest it's ever been for her to eat a brownie.

And listen carefully, friend. When you meet your Delores, when you encounter the person who does not really want to hear about your life or your strife but would rather tell you about hers, you have two choices:

1.   Walk away. Be done with Delores. Don't let her into your mojo.

2. Give Delores her brownie.

Otherwise, without having those two plans of action, you will leave Delores feeling depleted. Feeling guilty for ever complaining about a single thing in your life because you didn't know that Delores was going through such things. Feeling like you've just had life actually sucked right out of you with a syringe.

If all of the raindrops were life's troubles and brownies than we'd all be able to stand outside with our mouths open wide. But because that isn't the case and brownies have yet to fall from the sky, I think we just gotta take Delores for what she is.

I know that I almost always just listen, nod, and award Delores the brownie. Not to be fake or insincere, but because it would appear that this is what Delores needs. I feel like everyone deserves to feel like what is hard for them, *is* indeed hard for them. I have also realized that there is no chance that *I* am going bring Delores over to the bright side. She is not in a place to find contentment or happiness. She is not interested in moving forward.

In your mind, as Delores is in constant pursuance of the brownie, you must simply repeat, over and over: take the brownie, Delores. You matter, Delores. Your life must be harder than mine, Delores, because I don't feel as you do.

There will always be the brownie-needers, and no matter what realness they see or hear, will always feel that they have it harder than everyone. That surely, their existence has been markedly more challenging than yours or anyone else's. I honestly believe that those who are brownie-needers rarely even know their stripes.

You can either choose not to spend your time around those people, or you can choose to not let their need to bag that brownie bring you down. But when you are going through something that feels exceptionally difficult for your life or when you find yourself trying to figure out who to talk to when you are down, I'd recommend that you steer clear of Delores. She is not your girl. She will not help you get through. And she may only leave you feeling worse.

There are far too many people who you can go to who will never attempt to take your brownie. They are your folks for the hard parts. They are even a piece of the goodness in your hard.

When you meet a Delores, just let it go and let your little voice whisper:

Take the brownie, Delores. You win. You must need it more than me.

And go get yourself a cookie. With a Heidi. She'll let you have the whole thing.

LESSON:

The Second Wave May Come

The stories have come to me in emails and phone calls.

"...So they did a biopsy. And it's metastasized."
"...I had my mammogram. It's back."
"...There was a new mass. In the other breast."
"...The results are in from chemo. I had no response."
"...This is her third battle with Ewing's Sarcoma."

I want to talk about something that is hard for cancer patients and survivors. Something that may produce too much anxiety for those readers who are in fear of a recurrence. But as a survivor, I think that watching others encounter new mountains and climb them is part of the process of being a survivor of something. Once we've become a part of a "club," we're never getting out. Seeing others go through similar battles...or new battles, well, it's part of the process of moving forward in life in your *after.*

It is *the second wave.*

Life is full of this phenomenon. Of the *second wave.* The period in which, after you've become aware of something...after you've walked that mile in your shoes...*after.*

Patients like me. We have this *after*. This time where we are navigating the world after having endured early stage cancer. The time where our appointment schedule lessens. Where we have anniversaries that are one or two years or further out from *this*.

We are just standing up again. Rising. Getting our sea legs. Perhaps anxious at times about another wave mowing us down. But mostly, we're in the "cancer-free," "remission," or "no evidence of disease" categories with really insanely positive prognoses.

I am thankful that my cancer and my body have been responsive to my therapies.

But there are still days that make me anxious about the *what-ifs*.

What if the back pain means cancer is in my bones?

What if what I think is muscle pain is metastatic disease?

What if I have to go back there again?

This is the life of a cancer survivor. It's a glorious gift to get to be *through* it. But those what-ifs can be hard.

And then the second wave.

For me, as a survivor, as a young mom, as a daughter and a wife and a sister and a friend, *the second wave* is its own kind of hard.

I get to soak in the ocean of survivorship. I am enjoying the sunshine. I am just happy to get to be in the calm and enjoy the view in a different way than I have. But the second wave is rolling in.

Friends who I went through treatment with head into their anniversaries only to receive a report of recurrence. Friends who have been battling for a year are told they are advancing to MBCT (metastatic breast cancer thriver). Friends receive a first-time diagnosis.

Gosh. The second wave is hard.

It shouldn't be hard for me. I am not the one living the reality. I'm just living the news. But it's hard emotionally to watch my friends, these women and people I love and fought alongside, go through this *again*. I mean, I know they'll fight with everything they have once again, but as someone who received a different outcome, I find myself feeling guilt. I find myself sometimes stepping back because I don't want to seem like I'm shoving my calm ocean in their face.

If you've had a child, you might have experienced something similar. You get pregnant. Your friend gets pregnant. And then your friend loses the baby. There you are, pregnant. There she is, at a loss. It feels unfair. You might wonder, *why do I get to be so lucky,* as you watch the wave roll in and pull her down.

If you've watched a family bounce back from something incredibly hard, only to see the dad lose his job or the mother lose a parent then you know: it seems to come...in waves.

If you have a friend in their second wave...a friend who is once again feeling under water...just be *you* for them. Pray for comfort from anxiety and depression. Pray for them to live life through their treatments whether for Stage 1 or Stage 4 or something that has nothing to do with cancer.

This is hard. As a survivor it's hard. As a human it's hard. It's hard to watch people suffer. And the person going through the second wave is experiencing a completely different type of hard.

But. You are the person who is in the calmer waters; you can still feel your own joy. You are still allowed to be grateful for where you are. To use some of your positive energy to help others keep their heads above water when they feel like they are drowning.

If the second wave hits, the one who is in it may already be worn down, afraid, or over it. Lend them your love but not your pity. Give them your shoulder and your smiles. Be positive with them that they not only CAN but they WILL stand up to this wave, just as they did the first one, and they will ride it big time.

LESSON:
Lasagna isn't a Yard Stick

*L*asagna. Are you a fan? I would say I am, for the most part. When I was a child, I barfgagged any morsel of the creation that touched my lips. The mixture, at the time, was often made with cottage cheese, and the idea of chunks of curdled milk baked into a dish pretty much made me want to heave ho. But as an adult, I discovered the use of ricotta in place of cottage. And I also realized the beauty of how long a pan of lasagna can feed two people. Thus, a fondness for the dish grew.

If you've ever been sick, you probably know lasagna well. When my treatment schedule was determined, a friend of mine headed up a meal train, sent it out to every person she or I had ever met, and for six months, two to three days a week, food just showed up at my door, and filled our fridge and deep freeze. It was some sort of serious miracle.

By far, the most common delivery? Lasagna. It's easy to make. It's easy to bake. It has a mix of proteins and vegetables. And it keeps in a deep freeze for up to 34 years.

Lasagna. It is such a reminder of the time of my life that I can hardly even believe I got through. It is a reminder of being so tired I could barely keep my eyes open to eat. It is a reminder of being only strong enough to walk to the stop sign at the end of my block and back. It is a reminder of my fried taste buds burning from the marinara sauce. It is a reminder.

But hey, at least I got lasagna, right?
I know. I was *lucky* enough to have a Lasagna Problem.
Do you know what I mean?

A Lasagna Problem is what I call a problem that people try to provide rescue from. A Lasagna Problem is an illness or a loss or a something that has happened to you that you have been able to share with people. And in a way, even though a Lasagna Problem can be completely debilitating, at least you get the lasagna.

That's right. I just said *at least you get the lasagna.*

Because I have watched friends go through painfully awful battles...

Depression.
Addiction.
Disordered Eating.
Assault.
Postpartum Anxiety.
Betrayal.
Debt.
Broken relationships with a child. Or a parent.
And on. And on.

I've watched friends and family who have had to accept a horrific loss...

Of a child.
Of a marriage.
Of their home.
Of a parent.
Of their reality.
And on. And on.

Well after the initial impact, the aftershock shakes their ground time and time again. Day after day after day.

I've seen my friends sweating through day after day of a teething baby. Or deal with a teenager who is an asswad. I've watched friends try to juggle life as one parent is forced to carry the load while the other is slammed at work. I've seen dads try to muddle through a marriage that has been drastically changed by parenthood. People battling with toxic friendships. Others living months of colic with an infant. Moms who desperately want to stay home with their babes and are just not in a place to do so. Mothers who stay home and wish for the environment of a career.

I've seen a million types of pain, and a whole lot of it doesn't seem to garner a lasagna. A lot of it isn't accompanied by a meal train. A lot of it is chronic. With no real end in sight, a lot of pain leaves people wondering how many times they can be knocked down by the waves before they lose their hope in the undertow.

Suffering in silence or all alone, well, I imagine that to be a very different kind of hard.

I think people sometimes use the lasagna as a measuring stick. Like, *"Ohmygooooodness, my hard is not as hard as hers and so I must not mention it and I must keep it to myself and suffer in silence."* Or, *"I told people about my problems and no one is helping me."* Or, *"Everyone was here for me at the funeral but now, everyone's gone back to their lives and I am still here in this alternate reality of my life."*

Lasagna is not a measuring stick. If you do not have a Lasagna Problem, it doesn't make it any less of a problem, hardship, or stress. It doesn't mean that your probs aren't legit. It definitely doesn't mean that you are weak or unable to cope. And it sure as shit isn't going to simply go away if you just smile and act like it doesn't exist.

I know that Jay-Z talks about 99 problems, but for real, we all encounter a heckuva lot more than that in any given lifetime. We shouldn't have to let lasagna be one. Cottage cheese or not.

So, lasagna or none, your problems, your struggles, your suffering is real. Your growing and shedding and learning are happening. And what you perceive is hard does not need to be validated by anyone else because they are not walking around in your skin.

Lasagna is not a measuring stick. It might warm up your oven and your heart if someone drops one your way. But it doesn't label your struggles as real. That is up to you to determine. Don't minimize your stuff just because it doesn't have friends filling your fridge. You're probably just being saved from living a day where you can no longer handle another lasagna.

Oh, and if you are on the other side of things, be like my neighbor and maybe give someone a lasagna for no reason at all. Or maybe you could go with enchiladas. Or a rotisserie chicken. With a bottle of wine. Regardless of what the food is, to you, it could be a "just because" and to someone in your life, it could feel like every little and big thing that they've ever needed in that moment.

LESSON:

I Needed the Ocean

Three days after I turned 34, I had my mastectomy. It was the very end of February and I can recall, by that point, being *over* the cancer "journey." Also, I can't be completely certain but I believe that may be one of maybe 3 times I use the word journey in this whole book. I'm not really a fan of it after cancer. Maybe it's because it's also the name of a shoe store. Maybe it's because I really like the band. I don't know. But *journey* is not a word that I really dig. However, in this instance, it is, in fact, how I felt. I was *over* the appointments, the fatigue, the pain, and the constant showing of my boobs.

I still had work to do though. I had to heal from the surgery. I had to get my expanders filled. I had radiation ahead of me. And all I wanted was the ocean.

Every single time I checked in for an appointment, the receptionist would ask a few canned questions. Each time, one of the questions was, "have you been out of the United States in the last two weeks?"

UMMMMMM NO. Well, that's what I would say in my head. But usually, in responding to these people who were becoming my friends, I would jokingly say, "No! But someday, I'm going to answer yes to that question." When I imagined traveling again, I didn't ever think of *where* I would go. I didn't need it to require leaving the US. I just knew it had to have an ocean.

It was February, in Nebraska, which mostly means it's grey and cold. We moved into March which is still, often, grey and cold. April provides some hope of spring. May is the end of the school year. And in my cancer chronicles, that is when I began radiation.

For 28 days, I slathered up my chest with Aquaphor, picked out my music, and laid as still as possible while a grocery scanner pulsed over me, delivering cancer killing radiation in a targeted mapping on my chest.

My Rad crew included the same cast of characters and just like every other bit of my treatment, the nurses and techs became a bit of joy in my day. Radiation was not physically hard for me. But mentally, I was spent.

I needed the ocean.

I know. This is a curious statement from a person who has always lived in a landlocked state. I live in Nebraska for the people and the Dorothy Lynch salad dressing. But having fond memories of beach vacations and the mental release that salt water provides, I knew I needed to sit on the sand, hear the waves, breathe in the salty air, and feel the healing it brings.

For Mother's Day, Adam gifted me the very best surprise of all. He knew that we had blown our vacation budget on cancer. But he crunched the numbers and got the ocean on our calendars. Two and a half weeks after radiation was complete, we would be wheels up and on our way to the sea and sand. We would get to stay with some of my favorite people, my aunt Deb and uncle Hank.

I completed radiation. My skin began to heal. We headed to Florida for a quick weekend getaway. And I wore the damn swimsuit. Literally.

This swimsuit, the first one I'd worn post-cancer, was a rash guard and bottoms paired with a sun hat. Per Dr. Wahl's suggestion, I purchased two rash guards -- Lycra swim shirts with sun protection -- to keep my recently treated skin in tiptop shape. My boobs were built from expanders and were perky as could be. My hair, the style I'd named *the Ellen* for its short length and blonde color, was perfect for the beach. Everything felt worth celebrating.

Especially the ocean.

It was more incredible than I'd ever known it to be. I've always loved the sound of the waves. The blue of the sky. The sand beneath my hands as I place them behind me to hold me up. But there was something different this time.

In the past when I looked at the ocean I experienced a bit of agoraphobia. It was so big and so endless.

This time, in my blue rash guard with *the Ellen*, with scars and lines marked all over me, and a port in my arm, I looked at the ocean and thought about the fact that the ocean gets knocked down by itself, time after time, every single day and it keeps. on. going. That day, instead of the vastness seeming a bit overwhelming or the swimsuit bringing me fear, I was content.

The saltwater. The time with Adam away from the house where we'd lived cancer day in and day out. The laughing, late night beach walks, and skinny dipping with our hosts and my husband. It all truly felt like it had healing powers. To patch the areas of my heart that have been bruised by the reality that life is short. To patch the areas of my mind that were anxious or fearful about cancer returning. Or having to go through treatment again. To patch the areas of my soul that feel a bit of survivor's guilt, *why do I get to stay but a 2 year old boy doesn't.* The water, a baptism renewing the parts of me that had grown weary over the months of cancer.

And it was everything I needed. Everything my body needed to say, "that chapter has turned. a new chapter is beginning. And here it is."

We've soaked up the warmth of the sun since that trip. Once, when we received a great gift from Little Pink Houses of Hope for a week in Oak Island, North Carolina, and we experienced the ocean as a family for the first time. Another time when we drove our boys down to Gulf Shores Alabama for a spring break including Adam's parents that I hope none of us will ever forget. We've spent summer days at the pool or on the lake, taking in every bit of Nebraska sun we can get. And I will never grow tired of the life-giving properties that sunshine, fresh air, and water provide.

I will forever remember the first dip of my toes in the water post-cancer. Post-havoc. The sunshine after the storm. I hope I never to never forget the magnificence of feeling like I was seeing the ocean for the first time at age 34. Or at least seeing it differently than I've ever known it to be before.

LESSON:

You Have to Go Through It

When I was a little girl, I loved the car wash. Not the kind where you get out of your car and spray it down—and if you didn't know those existed then you clearly didn't grow up in a town of 1,500 people. I loved the kind of car wash where you drive onto a set of tracks, put your car in neutral, and then just let everything go on around you.

When I was in kindergarten, we had school every other day. I spent many of my off days running errands with my mom. Sometimes we'd drive into the capitol city. We'd grab a bite to eat, load our grocery cart at the Super Saver, and take our blue Volvo station wagon through the big-time carwash. I recall being completely enthralled as the water pinged hard on the metal of the car and the windows filled with abstract water designs. The big bristles brushed up against our vehicle. Eventually, a large dryer blew down on us as we neared the exit. And because we almost always got our car washed on a sunny day, or at least, a day without rain or snow, the doors on the other side would open and bam, we drove into a bright sunshine-y day.

Those simple days of childhood seemed filled with magic and they *still* seem filled with magic. But then there's reality, right? There's the errand you need to run, the groceries you need to get, the papers you need to fill out, the laundry you told yourself you'd put away four days ago. There's the stuff. And your car, even though it's clean on the outside and the salt and sludge have been washed off the exterior, it might still look like it's been ransacked by an entire basketball team on the interior.

A few years ago, in the fall, I entered the carwash. I'd actually been in a very sunny season in my life. I hadn't seen the storm coming. The day I got on the tracks, it was devastatingly dark. A flood of tears accompanied me in as the doors opened. I had a hard time getting my car lined up with the tracks. I received direction from those who knew those tracks well. I put my car in neutral.

But this carwash was not the type where I calmly viewed the soft dance whirring around me. Because this track was called treatment. I had cancer. I had made the choice to do treatment. And just as I'd been taught when I was 7 as we read, "We're goin' on a bear hunt," in the school library, the same was true with this cancer. I couldn't go over it. I couldn't go under it. I had to go through it. I had to align my wheels on the track, watch the door that went to my old life close behind me, and set my sights forward. To the sunshiney day.

It was odd at first, all the things whizzing around me. Everything was happening *at* me. My treatment plan was directed by a team who I'd only just met. And there was me, looking at the inside of my car—the inside of my life—and thinking that everything was just a huge mess.

The first round of chemo, when I met the Wildebeest, I realized that even if my car started to veer off the tracks, I simply needed to trust the powers that be. Because a wildebeest or a stay in the hospital were distractions that wanted to take my attention away from the ultimate goal—to oust the cancer. To Leave this time of my life with a clean bill of health. To exit the carwash with a shiny clean exterior.

That first-round hiccup led me to adjust my mirrors again. I needed to continuously check my blind spots. I needed to be right where I was in the carwash and stay on-track. Which required letting go. A *letting go*. And allowing the doctors and prayers and treatments to work their magic. All I needed to do was go through it.

Okay, so that's kind of minimizing the *going through* part, I know. Because the *going through*, man *oh* man, that shizz was an exercise in strength and patience. But I knew that if we did all the treatment and if that treatment worked...if I then had surgery to remove the hijacked jugs...and if I needed to do radiation and I adhered to the direction of the team...if we (myself. My husband. My boys. My family. My friends. My tribe.) did those things...the goal was a sunshiney day.

But I had to go through it first.

In the *through*, I met a thousand parts of myself that I didn't even know I possessed. I met a woman who was truly, madly deeply in love with mothering. I met a girl who still felt like she was as free as a 9-year-old. I met a confident storyteller who could impact others. I met a human who could find goodness in the hard. I met a warrior. So the through—even though it took might and must—I *had* to do the through.

I was lucky. Fortunate. Blessed. I was one of the lucky 1 in 8 who get breast cancer when, at the end of it all, I was declared cancer-free. I rang the bells. I celebrated good times. I was through.

After months of being on the cancer track, of being focused on moving forward if ever so slowly and surely, the doors opened.

It was a warmer season again. And though the sun may not have been shining brilliantly the day I completed radiation, the skies were blue and, after months of feeling on-track, I felt free.

At first.

I was done, right? Cancer was over, right? I was free to go back to my regularly scheduled programming. The car was clean.

Except the interior was still kind of a mess. Not like goldfish crushed into the carpet or crayons melted on the seats messy. More like empty water bottles rolling under the seats messy. With a layer of dust sitting on top of the dashboard. I wasn't even sure if I knew how to operate this vehicle anymore.

It should have felt like freedom. I should have woken up the next morning and said, "This is the first day of the rest of my life!" I should have hit the ground running.

But just because I'd made it through the carwash—the intense time of so many things happening around me, being orchestrated and directed by my people—cancer was still always going to be over or under me or somehow a part of my story and my stitching even if it was no longer a part of my body (praise the LAWD!).

The carwash is such a true representation of how I felt while going *through* cancer. I had to go *through* it. Chemo. Surgery. Radiation. Reconstruction. Having a whole crew manage that for me was the very best of a bad situation. But it broke down when the doors opened. Yes, I felt like I had accomplished the biggest feat of my life. Yes, I was thrilled to be done and to be past the internal warfare. Yes, I was thankful to be alive. Yes, I was happy to have one and a half nipples.

But I wasn't *over* it.

Just because we get through, or because we are surviving, or because we look all shiny and new on the exterior, that doesn't mean that we are through the emotions and grappling that comes with adversity. When you see someone who has weathered a storm in life, rarely are they truly *over it*.

The doors open and you have to figure out which way to go. You get to decide how to work on the other parts. You get to have your days of being sad, mad, anxious, or excited. You have to figure out what just happened…and how you are going to move forward. And the moving forward takes time. How much? I still don't know.

Guess what? Sometimes people get in the carwash and they get stuck there. This actually happened to my friend Stephanie. She got stuck in a carwash. Yes. An *actual* carwash. The door wouldn't open. In what is still one of the most hilarious stories I've ever heard in my life, Steph truly believed that she'd never get out of the machine when it malfunctioned.

Similarly but not at all hilarious, I have other friends who are stuck in treatment indefinitely. Friends who have been dealt a lifelong chronic diagnosis. Other friends who are metastatic breast cancer patients. And metastatic patients—a Stage 4 diagnosis—do not come with a timeline for *curative* treatment. It is, to date, incurable, which means that metastatic patients receive their diagnosis with an asterisk that says, *you will go in and out of the carwash over and over and over again*. Or, they will never truly get off the tracks. But they still have to go through it.

Steph got out of the carwash eventually, by the way. And I think the relief she felt was pretty great.

Because we do feel relief when we feel like the *hard* is over.

Be nice to yourself when your doors open. When you are free to roll right off the guiderails and you feel like everyone expects you to be past it. Because you will have a day (or a week or a God-only-knows-how-long time period) where you feel like you aren't thriving…heck, you are barely surviving. So allow yourself that day (or that week…).

When someone says to you, "Oh, so you're done with that hard thing?" And you're like, "Ummmmm ya. Sure! Totally. Uh huh!" but inside you are thinking, "It doesn't feel done with me," just know that they've never been where you are. They have, however, driven through their own mud that you may have never even thought of or experienced, and so while you're being nice to yourself, why dontcha just go ahead and be gentle with them while you're at it.

You have to go through it. And it all has to go through you.

When the doors rise and you are looking for the sun, know that the sun rises and sets each day. Sometimes it hides behind clouds, but just because you can't see it doesn't mean it's not there. It might simply mean that you need to adjust your speed, take your time, maybe even just park the car, and you will feel the warmth of its rays on your window when it's time. In your own time.

I take my boys to the carwash now. I see their faces and their eyes…I watch them so enthralled with everything going on around them. I remember how fascinating all the moving parts can be if you aren't focused on killing a horrid disease that has invited itself into your passenger seat. I remind myself that at the end, there will probably be sunshine. And that ultimately, no matter which way I go, I will eventually reach my destination. Even if it takes time.

LESSON:

It Can Take a Village to Build a Basket

In my early years of mothering, I tried to join a mom group. I say *tried* because I signed up, I paid, I went. For six months, I tried it.

I sat at a table with other moms, each week. And I liked them. But at the time, I wasn't open to them.

They were in a different place of motherhood than I was. They were in a three-kids-some-in-school-nothing-is-really-that-big-of-a-deal-just-enjoy-your-babies stage. Not in a condescending way. I think, at the time, I felt threatened by their ease with the *vocation* of mothering, and so I felt insecure in my own inability to find that ease. So I became a mom group dropout.

When I think of it now, I momentarily feel dumb for giving up. But just because my current self can see that, it doesn't change what my *then* self actually felt. Hindsight doesn't actually change the events of the story; it just changes our tone in how we read it.

Several years and two more children later, I, like I've heard thousands of other moms on social media express, was somewhat lost. I say *somewhat* because I loved my boys. From the first days that I held them, I felt like these people needed me and I, them. I loved my husband. I loved my life. But I also felt so overwhelmed by what so many moms seem to experience, which was the loss of *me*.

I felt like an unnatural woman, not *absolutely* eating up the joys of getting to nurture other humans. I mean, women had been having babies and being mothers for thousands of years, and yet, I didn't feel fulfilled by the feelings. I felt drained. Emptied out each day.

I had become some sort of a laundry sergeant. Every day. Laundry. Every day. Spray the stains. Detergent in. Wash on cold. Dry on normal. Fold. Fold. Hang. Fold. Snacks at 10 and 3. Lunch at 11:45. Naps at 1 pm. Bedtime starts at 7 pm. There were routines for everything, and everything felt routine.

Again. And again.

I was in a land of pumping and napping schedules and bedtimes and balanced snacks and schedules. Schedules. Schedules. Any sleep that I had once stockpiled from sleeping in on Saturdays until noon in the early years of marriage were a far-off memory I would retreat to in the middle of the night as I nursed and swaddled and hummed and rocked.

I should have been happy. I should have felt complete. Right?

This had been our goal. Children. Popcorn kids. Stairsteps. Whatever you want to call it when you attempt to produce children in a quick-moving cadence. By 32, I was indeed the mother of three healthy children. I, too, had weathered the pregnancies sans stroke or any major issues. All in all, we were calling that a win.

I should have felt as though I was exactly where I was meant to be. But I didn't. That didn't change the amount of overwhelm that I felt.

When we welcomed our third premature infant, and this one weighed three pounds, we were parents to three boys, all under 5 years old. And yes, I drank a fair amount of wine. I rarely showered. I cried a lot more than I remember having done before that. Maybe that was when my tear ducts started loosening?

For five years, I felt so focused on our goal of creating a family that I'd only really soaked up the present in the middle of the night while rocking back and forth or the holiday joys or the days that felt like they should be counted as all joy. And all of a sudden, we were *there.* The goal had been met.

Now what?

Oh. Yes. *Life.*

The *normal.* Our new normal as a family of five was here. I had controlled that, right?

So I continued that. Because that's what had gotten me through those early years with babes. Control.

I controlled the feedings. The naps. The routines. I felt like so much of mothering were the *have-tos.* Not the *get-tos.* I held on tightly to my duties while always thinking I should be giving more to them than I was. Every single day I wondered how or what I could do better or more to be everything that I was supposed to be for these tiny humans.

The calendar flipped to 2015. My boys were 6, 4, and 2. The Oldest was in kindergarten. The Middlest, preschool. The Littlest finally caught up from his early start. And ohmygoodness. There *I* was. I was able to actually sleep. And shower. It was time. It was time for me again.

I declared it a WHOLE new year. Yes, I did the word thing. I know. I'm so cliché. But it would be a year where I could just cruise for a bit. Where I could do some things to get myself in order. A year where I would do something for me every month. I got regular exercise. I enjoyed date nights with my husband who had stood right there with me through those baby years. I made a concerted effort for presence. I was feeling it again. A contentment.

In the fall, when the Oldest started first grade, I felt satisfied that I'd once again been in control. We were moving right along. Footloose. Fancy free.

Then came the lump.

The lump. The biopsies. My friend and carpool partner, Kristin, invited me to a mom group. A bible study. I'd never done a bible study before. I'd never thought I was *the type* who could sit amongst women who went to a group and talked about their faith. I had faith. I had always believed in God, but I wasn't *that* type, right? I was a swearing, sarcastic, sex-loving woman—one who had always been a Big Guy Believer but never one who could quote a scripture. Certainly I'd had a year for feeling whole, but was I holy enough to sit among the women in the group?

But there was the lump.
And suddenly, I had no more control.
I liked control, right? I needed control, right?
This unfolding of events shattered my illusion (or delusion) of any sense of control.
I went to the group.
I was diagnosed with cancer.

I went through all of it, and this group of near-strangers welcomed me each week as though I'd been there for always.

Suddenly, I was apparently the bible study *type.* And what do I mean by that? I mean I am a woman who attended a group that talked about the Bible. Hope that clears that up for ya.

Our bible study group was doing a study called "Seamless" by a woman who I'd never heard of named Angie Smith. As a person who hadn't ever tackled the entirety of the Bible, I found the study riveting. I found myself especially taken by the story of Moses.

I'm sure in all my years of growing up going to church I'd at one time or another heard the scriptures. But I definitely had not paid attention or committed it to the file in my brain marked, "Save for later. This could be useful."

Do you know the deets? If you do, way to go, you're cooler than me. If you don't, stick with me here.

So, long story short, Moses was born. His mama was trying to protect him. She made a basket out of dirt, leaves, and the like (yes, if you, too, are a mama having an aha moment because you just made the 'Moses+Basket' connection, I totally vibe with you). She placed little teeny tiny baby Moses in the basket and sent him down the river.

Ummmmm. What the heck? She sends her baby down the freakin' river?

Yes. This is the actual happening of the scripture and not some mid-day soap opera. But truly, to me at that time, it was just as riveting.

There I sat...bald...sans eyelashes...a 33-year-old mother to three boys under 6-years-old and I thought, "OH. MY. MOSES."

Not because Moses' mama had apparently been a badass at basket weaving (which leads me to believe she must have taken one of those underwater basket weaving courses that I've been hearing about for decades). Not because I thought she was a whackadoo for sailing her babe down the river, which in our day and age would 100% land you in the county jail. But because HOLY SHIT. Yes. Truly HOLY. This woman. This mother. She said, "God, dude, hey there...I trust that you are going to care for little Mo and you have got this." And she let go of the basket. What? She Elsa'd that basket. Yep. She *let it go*. She said, "I'm not gunna just pretend here. I'm not gunna just *say* I'm letting go." Nope. This woman fully let. It. Go.

That spoke to me.

When the idea of my life and my body being disrupted and destructed by cancer happened, I totally freaked the frack out. I will say it until I am blue in the face because it is never not going to be my truth: I thought I was dying. I thought 33 was it. I thought I was a vessel put on earth to bring my boys on board. I thought I was going to peace out, albeit not so peacefully or silently. I thought I was going to leave behind three boys who I loved more than I loved my Esprit sweatshirt in 1989 or my Dodge Neon in 1999. Even if I'd not fallen for motherhood right away, I'd fallen for *them* big time. And in going and getting cancer, I thought I was failing them big time.

I wanted to cling tightly to them. Not letting go for a single moment, moving forward because I wondered how many moments we would have. I thought about Moses' mom. I thought about my basket weaving duties. *I am their basket builder. I am the one who is supposed to, stick by stick and leaf by leaf, build their foundation. But I'm not ready to send them down the river.*

Then I realized that given my diagnosis of Stage 2A breast cancer, this cancer was most likely not going to kill me. In fact, I was educated on the fact that even with a diagnosis of Stage 4 metastatic breast cancer I wouldn't just keel over and die. (And as a side note: if research can be driven for metastatic disease, and a silver-bullet-curative-treatment could be identified then **every** person diagnosed with breast cancer would be told, *you will not die from this*. Wouldn't that be nice?)

I could cling to my boys. I could keep feeling the need to manage every bit of their lives and feel like it was my earthly duty to *do it all* for them. Or I could knock that shit off.

I chose the latter. If I wanted to live the crap out of life when I felt well enough to do so, I'd have to rest when I needed to rest. I'd have to hide in my room when germs were rampant. I knew that I also couldn't leave it all to Adam. It was then that I knew that if I couldn't be everything to my boys, I needed to trust that all the goodness of God, the Universe and our *village* was ready and willing. Willing to help in the weaving of their baskets.

I started looking at my trio through a different lens. I started reminding myself that so many of their actions could not be controlled by me. I started letting go. Not of them, but of the basket.

People offered to take the kids places for us. They offered to come over to our house and help. They offered to fold laundry. Make meals. Entertain the boys. They provided love and support and family and community for my children. Our families and good friends gave our boys answers and care. Strangers offered sunshine and positivity. I found that if the village was going to help us, I'd have to open the gate. So that's what we did.

We allowed our boys opportunities to learn independence because I did not possess the energy to puppeteer all the pieces. I continued my best to model behavior for them. Even from bed, I continued to communicate our expectations of them. We talked. Snuggled. Laughed. Cried. Read books. I still expected all kinds of greatness and wonder from them as humans. Because that was how I kept building their baskets. Giving them the foundation they'd need if ever Adam or I weren't right there through each day.

I knew that we had been building their baskets since day 1. And that even if danger threatened our family, they would and could still grow to be magnificent and loved. Just as they'd been since the pee stick showed *Pregnant.*

I didn't have to be the only person to ever put them to bed at night, because they adore when a grandma or a grandpa can snuggle them. I figured out that every time they spent time with their cousins, they returned with different sayings and doings. Fun life experiences that were forming their baskets. I saw that when they had one-on-one attention from people who gave up their lives to stay with us during the Crash days and post-surgeries that they were making memories that they'd never see as sad. Their baskets could also be strengthened and reinforced by our tribe, making them even more prepared for whatever twists and turns might be up ahead.

Through all those months, I realized what I hadn't in pre-cancer mom-life. I do not have to do all the things. I do not have to be all the things. Even though I am the mother of these boys and though I do believe it is my responsibility to love them and help them figure out this life thing, they don't need me to do it all.

I can love them unconditionally, allowing them to fail or learn, knowing they will still be loved. I can offer a safe environment, ensuring they don't turn brotherly brawls into UFC. I can repeat over and over that no one likes to look at pee all over the wall. But I do not need to be worried or anxious or overwrought with concern by all the little crap that just isn't going to matter.

My three sons. I am **one** really important person in their lives. But I am not the ***only*** important person. I hope that they will grow and eventually, they will go. As they grow from boys to men, I will know that while they are not mine to *keep* for life, they are mine to love for always.

Does this mean I plan to walk them over to a river bank and drop them into the water? Ummmm, no. We are not in imminent danger. Slow down, Sally.

But I can now trust that it's not just by my hands that their baskets are being built. That I don't have to hold on so tightly and feel overwhelmed by *having* to be their *everything*. They are loved. They are cared for. We have an entire village. That lesson has taken me from feeling all the have-tos to finding joy in just getting to be their mom.

LESSON:

Women Need Women

One summer I sat around a campfire with a group of women, most of whom I'd never met before that day. All of us were writers, which made the conversation all over the board. We talked about Tiny Homes. Foster care. Divorce. Marriage. And we talked about cows because what else do a bunch of women sitting around a fire in the middle of a cornfield in Nebraska talk about?

Okay. That's also not really fair.

We talked about cows because one of the women shares all of her adventures of ranching with the world and I, for one, find it fascinating, and thus had a million questions.

As we discussed the realities of rearing a herd, the Ranch Woman shared that when cows are in heat, meaning, when the women are having their monthly visit from Aunt Flo, these cows—the women at least—find comfort in being *very* close with one another (read: they grind up against their friends).

Yes. They hump each other.

When women cows are feeling randy, they nuzzle up next to another friend of the fairer sex and grind.

This sounds *odd*, right? Forget the fact that we're even talking about cows. Instead, imagine that you're hormonal and you want to cozy up to a gal pal and get all up in each other's biz.

As I sat there listening to the Ranch Woman talk about this, I both laughed until my belly hurt and felt that a little bit of life just made a whole lot more sense.

Something I've always believed to be true is that women—humans, cows, or otherwise—need women. Of course the female cows would find the ones they are most comfortable amongst when they are in their most vulnerable states. Of course they would find the women.

Therefore, like cows and creatures, and all things real and wonderful, women need women.

When I was a baby, I am fairly certain that I needed a womb to form in. Thus began my need for women in my life.

I am told that as a toddler, I wouldn't allow any other children to even be near my mother because she was mine. Because I was protecting my turf. Because I saw her as mine. I needed my mom. And today, I still do.

When I was a child, I needed my sister. I needed her on the daily. I needed her for a million different reasons. I needed her to be the other half of the most incredible roller skating dance performance to "I Think We're Alone Now" that anyone could ever produce. I needed her to be the other half of my Barbie world. I needed her to be the other one wearing the bows and paint-splattered matching stretch pants. She was and has always been my best of the best.

When I was in second grade, I needed a gentle, young, just-outta-school teacher to teach me about the power of a good book. About the beauty that can be found in our imaginations. About the way that creativity is intelligence. How kindness is the most human gift we can give.

When I was in fifth grade, I needed a strong teacher to sit and listen as I told her about my friend drama. I needed her to tell me that girls fight hard, but they can love even harder. That one day, those girls would start talking to me again. She knew that because she, too, had once been a fifth grade girl.

When I was in junior high, I needed the girlfriends who understood why I so badly wished for my period to come when all of them had already experienced it. I needed the friend who I called the day I got mine. Because even though it sounds weird to call someone when you get your period (because you have yet to understand that you will now bleed every month until further notice *and* you get to have a perma-seat on the Hormonal Express), she understood as she, too, possessed girl parts.

In seventh grade, I needed the girl who did my makeup and curled my hair before my first boy/girl dance. She helped me pick out the perfect hunter green+burgundy+dusty blue button-down to pair with my Doc Martens. The outfit that I wore as I danced in a circle with my besties to "Any Man of Mine." I needed the power of girlfriends in that time of my life where I was trying to figure out why it seemed so powerful and yet paralyzing to be a girl.

When I was in high school, I needed the women who coached me during two-a-days and on the weekends. The women who taught me that throwing like a girl was badass. That girls could be strong. That women can work together on a team and have fun and be successful. I needed my teammates, women who supported each other as they pushed each other.

I needed the girls in my late high school years who cruised downtown on a Friday night and understood that knowing the words to every single Aerosmith song was, at that time, just as important as knowing the periodic table. The girls who were my co-workers at the pool in the summers and listened to my boy adventures and assured me that my hair still looked dynamite seven bottles of sun-in later.

When I went to college, I needed the women who lived on my dorm floor. The ones who went to parties with me and the ones who made sure we all came home together. The ones who knew that I had little clue what alcohol was and that even though we'd all just met, women looked out for other women.

In my sorority house, I learned some of the most insane ways women rely on women. From sharing closets to test notes. From waking up in the early morning to cram to staying up late into the night hours, studying, laughing, making life out of the memories from delirious study sessions and late-night soul searching. I needed the women who were there to watch Sex and the City on repeat as I was on the cusp of girlhood to womanhood.

At my first job, I needed a woman who had been there, done that, and was willing to teach, be patient, and support me during my wild ride of trying to navigate the career-world and the married life. I found in that place, where I hung out with so many men— so many of my husband's friends who I also call mine—that I. Always. Do. Better. When I have women in my world.

I learned as I worked that women could be my biggest allies. My biggest cheerleaders. I learned that women can get a bad rap in the workplace. Yet I kept meeting women who wanted to mentor and raise up the next group of powerhouse gals. Those were the women I needed to learn from. I learned that I'd make some of my very best lifelong friends at an office. And in those very interesting relationships, they became like family.

In my twenties, I needed women who could party one weekend and stay in the next. As I transitioned to my thirties, I needed the women who would walk my screaming baby and know when I needed to be hugged, too.

When I became a mother, I needed women more than ever. I needed women who had already walked this path, like my mom and my mother-in-law who just *got it*. The ones who were currently in my shoes. The ones who hadn't yet opened the gate. I needed women around who told me my emotions weren't effing bananas...even if they were...because they, too, had the same effing bananas emotions. I needed women who loved every second of motherhood, and those who loathed it, to know that my somewhere-in-betweeness was in the range of *normal*. I needed my mother and my mother-in-law to remind me that this would be the hardest, best part of my existence. I needed friends who were not yet in the hood of mothers to remind me of all that I still was and all that I would still be, even as a mother.

When I began writing, I needed women. Women in scores. Women who saw my heart and loved me for it. Women who nodded in agreement and even the women who disagreed with my thoughts. I needed them all to be reminded that we are, each one of us, unique and fantastical people who have the super powers of femininity.

And of course, I needed women when cancer came. I needed women more than ever. Women who had also been under attack in one of the most feminine places on their form. Or, like the FUBC gals, women who had just begun their very own chapter. Women who had become nurses and doctors because they wanted to care for and educate women. Women who, even though a stranger, would send a t-shirt to brighten another woman's fight. Women who would clean my house, make us meals, and make me laugh, all in one day. I needed women who would sit beside me as I rested because they knew how scared I was that I might not wake up. I needed women to pray for me vigorously and carry me through. I needed women to step in and love on my children. To help my husband as he cared for me day in and day out.

I know that there are females who say, "I just don't mesh well with women." But there has never been a time that I have not needed *my girls*.

From womb to tomb, the saying goes. I believe it is truer than true that women need to be surrounded and grown among women, from our very beginning until our very end.

We are meant, I believe, to be in community with women. To meet them. To listen to them. To learn from them. To support them. We are meant to sit around with them into the wee hours as we watch fireflies in the summer sky and soak them up as our *sisters* in this life.

Women need women. Whether it's to talk when the day is long, or to cry when the years are short. Whether it is to contemplate the deep dark depths of the universe or talk about Tom Hanks and Rita Wilson being the only couple that will last. In the boardroom and in the labor and delivery room. Sitting next to you holding your hand or holding your hair after a too-fun night or after a day in the chemo chair. As we welcome babies and say goodbye to loved ones. Whether we are killing it at work or staying home with a crew. If we are married or not. Four-years-old or four decades old. We need to find the ones who *get us* and get us good. And when we do, when we find the friends and the females who empower us, enrich us, and feel like we can't do life without them, we need to thank our lucky stars, cozy up to them, and tell them our life is made more complete by their presence in it.

The cows, they get it. They know that their very basic need is to be close to and in community with those who get them the most. Especially in those times when they *feel* the most. And the grinding, I'm just gonna go ahead and assume that's no different for them than it is for us to have a Friday night out with drinks and deep convos. Because really, cows are just like us, right? And women, they are, too.

LESSON:

I Am Worth My Time

*B*arb. The name of my therapist is Barb. I'm a big believer in therapy. Especially when life comes on ya like a ton of bricks. Then I believe in lots of therapy.

I went to therapy twice in high school when my mom heard me throwing up through the bathroom door. I only went twice and that was it. I felt like I could work through it on my own. I felt like therapy was for people who had *real* problems. I determined that between sports and clubs, *I didn't have time.*

I didn't seek out a therapist in college and struggled with balancing school and growing up. I had Monday night meetings and 16 credit hours. *I didn't have time.*

I didn't find a therapist when I moved to a new state after getting married. I was struggling with figuring out how to cope with life having changed so much in such a short amount of time. I didn't know if our insurance covered it and was too busy to investigate it. *I didn't have time.*

I thought about finding a therapist after motherhood but it all felt overwhelming. I figured I'd just muddle through. That this too, would pass. Because after all, I had mouths to feed and minds to form. *I didn't have time for therapy.*

I'm sure there were a million other days in my life that could have benefited from a little self-reflection or a big intervention. But each time I thought about actually *doing* therapy, I decided I didn't have time. Time as a human can feel at such a premium that taking an hour to sit down and just talk about myself somehow felt like a luxury. And I sure as heck didn't have time for luxury.

It wasn't until I was assigned an entire team to heal the rest of my body that I finally understood I deserved to have someone help my brain, too. I no longer saw it as a luxury but a necessity to my ability to thrive. I asked for recommendations and found myself on the schedule with Barb, a psychiatric nurse practitioner who, for the bulk of her career, had specialized in oncology.

My first appointment, I went through almost an entire box of tissues. I felt like a maniac. I wondered if me, sitting in this chair bawling, going through a box of tissues was really *worth* my time. I was certain Barb would see how weak I was. I was afraid she'd tell me that my feelings weren't right or valid. That I was processing it all incorrectly. But as I wiped my tears and my nose as our first session came to a close she looked at my pile of discarded tears and smiled. "That's good work!" she said.

She was right. Therapy, feelings and freeing them, was absolutely *work*. But I liked it. I liked her. I felt like she knew her stuff. I felt like she got me. Therapy and the time spent doing therapy, to me, felt useful. Like a process worthy of my energies. I wished that every single person going through treatment, heck, every single person going through *life* could know that therapy is not a luxury but a necessary cog in the processes of healing and dealing. No matter what you are healing from or dealing with.

Therapy, for me, has become important work.

GOOD work.

I know now, more than I ever realized before, that I *do* have the time to do this work. I always have. But now I actually choose to give it my time. Not because I'm some sort of woman of leisure who sits around drinking frappuccinos all day and ordering things off of Amazon and have nothing better to do with my time. But because I'm just a normal woman and my life depends on it. My health depends on it.

Because sometimes health takes work. And drugs.

There will be some who disagree with that statement. Some who believe that medicine and interventions have no place in our lives. That was not the direction my treatment took. For me, for my diagnosis and my prognosis, I was interested in the age ol' approach of following protocol and occasionally, "Throwing all the shit at the wall and seeing what sticks." Sometimes *shit* means medication. Sometimes *shit* is new agey. Sometimes it's spiritual. Sometimes it's physical.

My treatment, survival, and thrival, have included medications, exercise, diet changes, therapy, alternative therapies, and tequila (preferably Patron). It's meant taking care of the place where cancer began, every part of me that it has touched, and the body that is moving forward with me. There have been shots to manage my hormones, pills to manage my anxiety, stretches to handle my soreness, and even pot to handle my pain. I've prayed. I've studied meditation. I've plopped myself into a sensory-deprivation tank. And I've done therapy.

My Thrival Plan. The day-to-day *work* to try to stay well in body and mind.

I'm not sure why it took cancer to get me to focus on thriving. On putting in the *good work* of therapy, seeing my doctors regularly, and claiming my oncologist's suggestion of at least 150 minutes of exercise a week as my *"prescription."*

I'm not sure why it took so long to realize I had the time.

Okay. That's a lie. I know why.

Because life.

And marriage.
And motherhood.
And being human.
House stuff.
Errands.
Finances.
Netflix.
Hulu.
Prime Video.
Instagram.
Obligations.
Commitments.
Time.
And on. And on.

Life has a lot of moving parts, right?

A lot of time takers.

Cancer forced me to see that even when life is full, we ought to include ourselves on our list of to-dos.

I still love all those things. The time takers. Specifically in that first little category. Okay, and the third because Netflix = *oneofthebestthingsevertohappen*. But the reality is—and I am *so* not the first person to say this—we all make time for the things we want to *give* our time to. And while I don't think we need to be in the number one slot on the dance card, it would be nice if we gave ourselves a spot.

We forget to remind ourselves of this at the end of the long day.

After a jillion meetings at work.
After the dog had an emergency visit to the vet.
After being stuck in traffic.
After a kid barfed while eating our home-cooked meal.
We forget to remind ourselves...

I AM WORTH MY TIME.

Before my life, my future, and my family were threatened, I didn't *pay myself first*. Before my *being here* was in jeopardy, I didn't give myself my time. Because taking myself out of the schedule gave me one less thing to schedule. I felt like I could wait.

Take the time now.
Make a plan to thrive.
Or, at the least, to figure out how to put one foot in front of the other.

Remind yourself that putting in the *work* is not a luxury. *Good work,* and you, are always worth your time.

LESSON:

Screw Busy. Get Full.

How many of us open our eyes in the morning and reach for our phones? I know I do. I grab for my phone after reluctantly opening my eyes. I rise in the morning, feet to the ground, and if necessary, confirm that the other inhabitants of our little corner of the world are up and running.

Getting ready for the day, I run through my mental list of all things marked "to-do" in my head. There are meetings. Meals. Practices. Deliverables. Action items. Writing. Listening. Parenting. Planning. Driving. Corralling. It's always something.

Because life. If you wake up for it, there's probably stuff that's gonna need to be done. And every day that I get to reluctantly open my eyes, I have to remind myself, once again, that *yes,* I am, in fact, pretty lucky to be able to do that. *Because cancer.* Cancer put the brevity of life in the forefront of my windshield and every day when I wake up to do life again—even if the day ahead includes a child who is whining about not knowing where his reading sheet is or a shit-ton of to-do's or a pile of work—I find that I am content knowing I get to be here for it.

Why yes, I *am* aware that I have grown into a human cliché.

I'm good with that because of that moment I have each morning...the one where I silently recognize that I'm getting to go another round...where I find peace with my to-do's. Because I gave up being busy.

Yes, I know. *Bold agenda, woman,* right? Well, here's my rationale:

Life is not just busy work.

I've gotten into a habit of going through my boys' backpacks every day. Sure, I know they could easily do this, but I kinda like getting a first look at whatever they brought home from the day. I am able to snag anything that I definitely want to hold onto for future blackmail needs. I get to take stock of how much of what they did at school that day was really useful. And how much was just busy work.

Busy work...something that the teacher has to assign them for some sort of requirement...is nothing new. It's been around for a long time and it very well might have been created by a mother trying to figure out how she was going to get herself a damn shower. She was probably dirty, staring into the eyes of her toddler and thought to herself, "WAIT. If I just give him a few sticks to play with, that'll keep him busy and I'll get clean!"

Busy work is sometimes necessary. In school. In motherhood. In life. But I don't think that busy work should be our life's work.

Instead, I think we should be full.

Yes, in a time where so many people are urging you to cut back, I am recommending that we all get nice and full.

Think about a time when you had a wonderful meal out with friends in a cool city. You all shared appetizers and drinks and when you left, you thought, "My belly is happy. My heart is happy. And that night was good for the soul."

When I think of *full* that's what comes to mind.

When I first decided to screw being busy, I took a look at my calendar and said, "Hmmmmm...what are we doing because we feel like we *should* be doing but we totally don't derive any real value from other than maybe keeping up appearances or checking a box?" Those were the first things to go. Hasta la vista to should-ing all over our calendar.

The very best thing happened. Our calendar was still, at times, packed.

But it wasn't because we were busy. It was because life was full.

I'm seriously not just being flowery.

I'm being honest.

When I started saying, "Nah. Not interested," to the stuff that had really just become the busy work, the rest of our commitments felt like *want-to* or *get-to* things rather than shoulda stuff. Things that are front and center? Weekends filled with sports events. Seeing friends and family. After-school times filled with kids at our house or club pick-ups and drop-offs. Evening practices. Night times filled with dinner and reading before bed. To some, that might sound busy. But to us, for our family...the little microcosm that we are growing through life with...it feels full. We *like* the sports stuff that our kids like. We *like* to be able to see friends and family and make memories and be in a community with people. We *like* the things we are saying yes to. We enjoy them. They fulfill us. And because of them, our calendar, and our life together, is full.

Once I'd made a commitment to be done with the bulk of the busy work, I have felt much less weighed down by expectations of others. Now, when I say yes to doing something, it's generally something I want to do. It sounds like a luxury or a fairy-land, right? A place where you just say no to the stuff you don't really vibe with and yes to the things that fill you up?

But seriously, it's life, people. And it's up to you to decide if it's yours or not.

You can say no.

You can say, *not right now*, and come back to it later.
You can say yes.
But you do not have to commit to *busy*.
YES, busy work will always exist.

There will, as mentioned previously, always be laundry. There will be tasks that are, no matter how you do them, *chores*. There are *jobs*. And *work*. There will be moments where you are hanging by a thread and you put a show on so you can just eat a piece of cheese in silence. Sometimes we just hafta *adult*. But when those things can be the filler flowers mixed in the bouquet that is your existence rather than the show-stopping stems, you might even feel like you have a moment to stop and smell the roses.

Screw being *busy*. Make a point to survey where your energy is being spent and determine if your choices are sucking the life out of you or filling you full. Life is meant for so much more than busy work.

LESSON:

For Better or For Worse is Pretty Vague

For better or for worse. We were 23 and 25. I was fresh out of college. He was one year into his first post-degree gig. We were crazy goo-goo ga-go hopelessly head-over-heels for one another. Marriage and a life together and the whole "for better or worse" contract seemed like the most logical step.

So *better* or *worse?* At that juncture in my life, what did I envision as the day-to-day moving forward of our two lives? What could that cover? Losing a job. Being annoyed by one not loading the dishwasher appropriately...or the other leaving socks on the ground when there are laundry basket drop points at every doorway. Not liking a job. A favorite show getting cancelled on ABC. No longer being able to host *Lost* Wednesdays?

We didn't really know, honestly. Like, not only did we *not* know. We didn't *know.* I mean really. In today's times when the majority of us are picking our own spouse without any sort of parameters, really, marriage is kind of a universal crapshoot. Obviously, the big goal is to say the vows, do the marriage thing, have it work out, suffer no major injuries and *happily ever* after, right? But it doesn't always work out that way. So maybe we chose to tie our horse to the right wagon or maybe not.

We decided to go with the wedded bliss option and in April of 2005, the man who I was hot-n-heavy over and I got hitched. In front of 700 people. Yes, 700 people. Which stemmed out of the fact that normally 60% of those you invite to your wedding attend unless, apparently, you get married in the wedding off-season, then 102% will show up and you will basically be hosting a large kegger. It will, however, be the best day of your life with almost every person you love, so, all in all, *winning.*

But yes. 700 PEOPLE were sitting butts in the pews as we looked each other smack dab in the eyes and said our vows.

"For better or worse. For richer for poorer. In sickness and in health."

We said these blanket statements that most people say at the altar. We added in a few other flowery words of our own. But mostly, with a hope, a prayer, and a, "I take you as my one and only for all eternity," exchanged, we were bound by marriage and God.

I don't think I ever really thought of the fact that someday, we'd actually have a worse to our better, a poorer to our richer, and sickness to our health.

I can't help but wonder at times, what if we rewrote our vows, went back to the beginning and stood, again, in front of hundreds. Would he say yes to it all? Would I? Would he have signed up for all of it?

Would he have vowed to love me through my hormonal ups and downs? Through not only the glorious second trimester of me carrying his child but the hideous first trimester wherein I morphed into a monster? Would he have vowed to hang around and wait on me hand and foot as I served my first bed-rest sentence and then to be on team Crazy Train as I was certain the pain of birthing our first child would end in me walking to the light?

Would I have agreed to be the errant sock collector and the receipt sifter as long as we both would live?

Would he have said, "Yes. Yes. I support you going to Target when you've had a bad day and just need to get diapers+candy corn+groceries+a pair of jeans off the sale rack."

Would he have stood up in front of my family and said, "Yes. I take your daughter to be mine even when she can't seem to spatially manage a dishwasher."

"Yes. I will honor that she is a creative and wild heart on a stick and that she follows her heart first, always. Even though I am more of a brain-following guy."

"Yes. I take her to be my wife and my one and only when she wears the same shirt to bed and for the following day and for bed the next night because, actually, I find not having to run the washer as often really socially conscious."

"Yes. I will absolutely love and honor and cherish her when she is wearing diaper pads post-birthing one of our humans. When her nipples are bruised and sore. When she cries every time I leave the house. I am **totally** stoked for that."

"I will love her even when her body is being attacked by cancer and I'm scared I might lose her."

"Yes. I will love her. In sickness. And in health."

We didn't say, "With hair or without. With or without breasts. You will love me and I will love you whether I can work or not. Even when you have to carry the load while I get well. Even if I never get a chance to repay you."

Can you imagine if our vows had said, "In times where I need you to run to Walgreens for suppositories, Gatorade, and MiraLAX. In the moments where I need you to be my balance as I squat over the toilet, wearing a surgical bra and two drains from surgery. You must promise that in those moments you will continue to cherish me."

What if we said, "Please, dear, promise to love me in all of the human-ness that I possess. In the times where I'm having a day. Where I cry at the dinner table. Where our children ask, 'Why is mommy crying?' I promise I'll legit love you in those moments if you, too, will legit love me."

Or perhaps, "I promise to celebrate your highs and be there for you to lay your head on my shoulder during your lows. I promise to cheer when you finally poop out something that sounded like a small child into the toilet. I promise to get you more toilet paper if necessary. I promise to still think you are as hot as you were on our first date. Even though I now know you poop."

I mean truly madly deeply. In all that could happen to happen in life, saying to one person, "Ya. I'll do your shit with you and I'll even make it mine." Well. That's a pretty big thing to say and vow and roll with.

From the shit to the rainbows, the man I married, the man who took me for better or for worse has taken our vows to heart and to fart. And I wouldn't have ever even known to ask for all of that when he proposed.

My husband. He signed up for this, *yes he did*. For **me**. We both did. The vows, the little sentences we strung together in front of 700 friends, those were pretty much generalized statements saying, "Yep. I'm in it to win it even if shit gets real." But not a day goes by where I'm not thankful for how seriously he takes the footnote: *and ALL other duties as assigned.*

Through cancer and motherhood and everything that has been added to our life together, I sometimes wonder if he had to do it all over again, would he choose to tie his horse (not a euphemism) to this wagon? But when I ask him why he's so good to me, he always replies, "'Cause your ma girl."

He has been put through the ringer in our time since we've shared our nuptials. Not a night comes where I don't put my head on him and value what we have. Not a morning occurs where I don't thank God that this man has stuck through it. The crazy train. The carwash. The good times and bad. The joy and the joyful. The sickness, the health, the richer, the poorer, and the better and worse.

I tell him every day, "I respect the shit out of you," because, well, it's true. And I love him quite madly, too.

For better or worse is actually pretty vague. But maybe, for all of us humans, that vagueness can become the best gift ever.

LESSON:

All the Days Are for Dancing

When I was 7, my sister and I would spend HOURS making up roller skating routines on the cement slab that served as a basketball court for my brother in our backyard. Sure, the basketball court was probably intended for my sister and I as well, but we were more into the smooth skating surface than the hoop and net. We had a little boom box (aka, tape player) that would bust out our music. There were a few tapes that we would alternate between, the main one being some mix of '50s and '60s songs that I'm assuming we somehow acquired from our dad's collection. The songs included Oldies like, "The Wanderer" and "Runaround Sue." And even though that was about the only time in my life I've dug "The Wanderer," even in my late 30s, anytime I hear the song it takes me back to the cement slab behind the blue '70s ranch on 6th street.

Music is legit powerful. It makes me nostalgic. Sentimental. Music gets *in* me. Music makes me dance. And dancing is like a dose of goodness.

Just like Kenny Chesney says in his song "I go back."

Back to so many moments of happiness.

...Dancing in the kitchen with my mom and dad, "Gypsy in My Soul" on the tape player.

...The school auditorium, feet on the seat in front of me, listening to my brother sing Billy Joel.

...The cafeteria in sixth grade, playing Crash Test Dummies on a purple Sony with a black strap.

...Summers spent lifeguarding, my friend Abby playing DJ, and Deanna Carter playing over and over.

...A little Red Dodge Neon, sitting in the passenger seat, windows open, my sister behind the wheel, "MMMBop" on the speakers.

...Turning my tassel in the year 2000 and "Jack & Diane" ushering us out of the school gym.

...Standing in a circle with my sister around my newest sister, swaying back and forth to "When you Say Nothing at All."

... 626 N 16th street, the address of my Sorority house in college, with "Sunshine, Lollipops and Rainbows" blaring over the house speaker at 7 AM.

...Our wedding, swaying to the beat, looking into each other's eyes, singing the words to "Feels Like Home."

...Our honeymoon, lazing by the pool with the sunshine and Bob Marley.

...My days in Austin when I first heard The Killers and Coldplay live in concert with my co-workers.

...Holding our firstborn the day after he arrived, listening to Jack Johnson and knowing that I loved him already.

...The moment our second came into the world, my birthing playlist tuned to Chris Tomlin.

...The time after I had our third and I heard lyrics by Conor Oberst and found myself stuck on them for a lifetime.

Music, for me, is like some sort of quantum leap. It can take me from the present day back to a past moment. It serves as an instant reminder of the life I've lived.

Is it that way for you? Do you have your own mixed tape of memories?

If I grabbed the cassette of my songs, of those songs, and named it (don't pretend you don't have a CD somewhere labeled Friday Night Vibes) it would be called, *Days of Innocence.* Because while there were no soothing sounds of Enya included, it was a time before I knew I'd have cancer someday. It will always be music that took me back to *before.*

Before the day that every song I heard made me want to curl up in a ball and cry. It made me so upset because cancer seemed to seep into everything, tainting the magic it had always provided. Even music, one of my favorite things, was being attacked by this monster in my life.

My friends Karin and Grant made me a CD. Yes, a CD. (For my children, if you are reading this book for the first time in the year 2026, a CD is a small disc that magically holds music and plays the tunes on a device called a CD player. Call Grandpa E. and he'll show you one.) The picture on the case was an impressive image of our whole family donning pink boxing gloves. *Ashli's Fight Songs,* the label read. Each song was to be listened to on a specific day.

All music for *my* fight. Songs about being a warrior and not giving up. Songs to pump me up for the big moments. Sentimental songs about being a hero. Songs to dance to, of course. Because I always always loved to dance.

But so many songs made me cry. The day I'd had my mammogram, "I Hope You Dance" filled the ballroom at a wedding and I lost it. I could not listen to anything remotely sentimental. I played and sang "How Great is Our God" with my head bare, and my voice cracked with emotion. Heck, I couldn't even handle "Eye of the Tiger" without breaking down. I'd forever been deeply connected to music and yet I could barely listen to the radio or a mixed CD without turning into a blubbering basket-case of emotions.

Until the moment I got the music back in me. The day that I claimed a fight song.

Literally. The song that got me dancing again was "Fight Song." The tune by Rachel Platten had become a hot hit the year prior and was what we put on the night we cheers'd in our kitchen, all five of us, after I'd had a visit to my doctor earlier that day. The visit had included a physical exam of my breast and my doctor said, "While we didn't gather any pathology, I feel as though after one chemo your mass has already taken a hit. It feels as though it has shrunk."

That news had me in the mood for a good ol' fashioned celebration. So we turned the Sonos on full-blast, filled up our finest flutes, and we—my husband, myself, and the 6, 4, and 2-year-old—danced. We smiled. We laughed. We twirled.

I had a port in my arm. No hair on my head. My energy had just resurfaced after a brutal first round chemo experience. "Fight Song" played and I felt the fight in my heart.

In that moment, I went back. Not to a certain song or a moment. But rather, to the dancing. To all the moments of dancing.

...The dancing that he and I, this man who I'd married, had done at our wedding.

...The dancing that we'd shared over the decade + that we'd been married.

...The dance he'd done each night to lull our Oldest to sleep over the first six months of his existence.

....The dancing I'd shared with the Middlest at Kindermusik class, his face full of joy, his blue eyes giant with elation.

...The dancing I'd watched the two Olders do via video while I was home on bed-rest with the wee one.

6

...The mid-day dance parties I'd shared with the Middlest and Littlest while the Oldest was off at school.

...The dance we had on a Saturday morning amidst laundry and a sticky kitchen table following the realization that we'd lost a pregnancy.

The song played, we danced in the kitchen, and I felt the magic. Pictures flashed through my mind. Pictures of the life that we have formed together. Just like we did before we compiled that album of mental pictures, we danced. And I was reminded that through all of it...the hard, the joyful, the momentous, and the mountains we were begging to move...we'd danced. I reminded myself that as long as I could remember to breathe, I needed to remember to dance. I needed to keep adding to my soundtrack.

We danced and we were happy. I felt something that wasn't anxiety or fear. I felt joy.

"Fight Song" was my gateway drug back to music. After that night, music no longer reduced me to tears. *NO.* Instead, it once again became a way I felt alive.

And the songs played on.

"I Lived" by One Republic. I listened and danced to the words and claimed them as a personal theme song.

I cried. Gosh darn it. I know I just said that music no longer reduced me to tears. Well, I suppose I lied. But this time, I cried happy tears. I cried because I'd been missing the comfort of music. I cried because I hadn't realized how much I'd *needed* the magic back in order to move forward.

Treatment moved forward. It continued to prove effective. We added more songs to the playlist. We danced.

Every day that I had enough energy, I danced.
My tribe right there, dancing with us.
We danced after chemo.

Sometimes even in chemo (which of course the nurses loved because I was attached to an IV Pole. I suppose it's a whole new interpretation of pole dancing).

Celebrating each milestone of treatment. I lived. Sweet baby Jesus, I was so *alive*.

I'd been unable to exercise throughout chemo. My white blood cell counts were too low. My weight was too low. I needed every calorie I could hold onto. My stomach was too wrecked. My metric of energy in the days following each round included walking to the stop sign at the end of my block and then making it back to the house. And dancing. Always dancing.

Following my sixth and final round, when I knew we were through the storm, I asked my oncologist if I could run a race. I explained that with chemo behind me, I wanted to move my body. I wanted to run before I went under the knife. I wanted to run before my boobs took me down and out again. Cancer had run my life for far too long, I explained to him. He said, "Absolutely. Yes. Go live!"

So on Super Bowl Sunday, a frigid Nebraska winter morning, Adam and I showed up for a 5k. After having our lives run by cancer for the last 20 weeks, the two of us, side by side, ran cancer.

In my mind, through the entire race, I envisioned the five of us dancing in the kitchen. Warm breath sat on the cold air. I played one song, over and over. For 3.2 miles. One foot placed in front of the other time and time again. *Just. Keep. Moving. Forward,* I coached myself. I listened to the words. Tears warmed my face as I crossed the finish line. *I LIVED.*

I was living. *I had lived.* I would continue to live. I knew that I would often feel out of control. I knew that some days would feel really hard. I knew that most would include at least one pinch of goodness. I knew that some days I would run my life. Others, it would run me. But in all of it, I would live.

We continue to dance. In the kitchen on Friday mornings to Panic at the Disco. In the car as I blast "500 Miles." Around the firepit with Zac Brown Band. And forever, to Van Morrison reminding us of "These Are the Days."

I felt such a void when the music was gone. It was such a good day when the music returned. I'm so grateful that my album keeps adding tracks. The songs play on. And whether a day is hard or long or joyful or short, I will never again let myself forget that *all* the days are for dancing.

LESSON:

Listen, Learn, and Get Better

If you ever want to feel perpetually young, get diagnosed with breast cancer at age 33. Actually, I don't wish that on anyone. But as the many gal pals I've gained through my diagnosis, treatment, and survivor-life can attest to, one of the most common statements you hear as a woman with cancer who has not yet gone through her menopausal years is, "But you're so young."

It's quite the confidence boost.

Okay.

Not really. But let's call it that, huh?

Being not even mid-life when you hear your life might be ending can really feel like its own crisis. But it can also propel you into overdrive, constantly collecting the lessons of your adversity in an effort to find some sort of purpose in the pain. All the things that, should you get to move forward, you will use to—as my husband repeats day-in and day-out to our boys—*listen, learn, and get better.*

As I went through chemo, I also went into menopause. It's pretty common for women receiving chemotherapy for breast cancer, a sometimes hormonally driven diagnosis, to find their hormones in hibernation. Whether it will go back to normal, well, there's not really ever a for sure.

As I completed my initial treatment plan I then chose a five-year plan that would suppress my ovary function (aka, put them to sleep) and keep me, from ages 34 through 39, in chemical menopause. I've experienced hot flashes, dryness in my veeg, and a whole mixed bag of random stuff. It has provided head scratching symptoms (literally, my scalp is drier than my Sister Downstairs) and lots of comic relief. It's just another thing I learned about breast cancer that I never knew before.

But, luckily, I also rarely have to wear deodorant *or* shave my pits. I don't have to deal with tampons or period underwear. And taking the estrogen and progesterone out of my body makes cancer less likely to have an abundance to feed on.

I think the weirdest part of going through cancer and menopause as a young woman is that in so many ways, I am still a young human. I feel like I'm just not *there* yet: to the place of wisdom and worldliness like many of my more naturally menopausal counterparts. And while I've learned a lot and lived a lot over the last few years, I still feel like Britney Spears standing on the top of a boulder, arms wide open telling the sky that "I'm Not a Girl, Not Yet a Woman" (which also happens to be one of my favorite karaoke songs).

I still feel like I'm the kid in the movie Big that shrinks back down from Tom Hanks and suddenly, he's a young boy walking down the street draped in big, oversized clothing. I know. I'm not a boy. Or a child at all. But I feel sometimes like the whole being in menopause, having cancer-spective, and knowing what it is like to seriously think you might keel over and end up in a casket makes for a weird juxtaposition of thoughts when you're not even 40—an age that you have long thought of as only being the middle of your life. I can't help but wonder if I will forever feel young, always feel older, or if I am just aging at a normal life-pace, and am just not there yet.

Like, will I always be unorganized and unfiltered? Or, at age 50, will I mature into a responsible human who actually answers text messages in a timely manner and doesn't laugh whenever someone says the word *balls*?

In some ways, I feel like I've morphed and grown. I find myself less frazzled by the little stuff than I used to. In others, I feel like I'm still a child, needing my mom, my husband, and therapist to talk me through the days when that fear of recurrence rears its head.

In some respects, my body is older than me—like the fact that I do have some biological "signs" of menopause's effects on my Downtown Sally Brown. On the flipside, my boobs just became toddlers as they've only been around for the last couple of years.

There are days where I feel like I'm an old soul who *only* wants to listen to James Taylor and Simon & Garfunkel on repeat. Others days, I dip my toe in the millennial fountain and want nothing more than podcasts playing in the background.

Sometimes I feel like I'm pretty crunchy, drinking kombucha, sipping bone broth, and using Thieves to clean every surface. Others, I am oh-so conventional, getting my hair colored, shopping at Big Box stores, and popping sugar-coated calcium gummies.

Every so often I look put together, wearing something that might be found in a store that currently exists. Mostly I wear some sort of expanda-wear that I might have also worn to bed the night before.

I often think about how it would be to raise our boys in a small community like the one I grew up in. And in the next breath, I'm all over the conveniences of living in a more populated area.

There have been periods of time where I posted on social media a number of times a day. I loved how it can bring people together, form a community, and promote *goodness*. And then there are other times when I slowly stopped checking in and suddenly realized I didn't miss it at all.

I have days where I feel like my boys have gotten so big and others where I see them as still being my babies. Periods of time where I feel like I want them to be kids for as long as possible and others where I wonder if I'm doing enough to keep them on par with the kids of this generation.

I will sit down to write about the funniest part of my day only to end up writing a lyrical thoughtsy mind-dump of feelings. I am often loud and outgoing yet prefer nights in, cozied on the couch, watching Sleepless in Seattle.

I believe in prayer and God. I also take medication to even out my anxiety and listen to meditations to help me feel calm.

I love that I get to be aging into my late-thirties and will happily celebrate every year of getting older. But I also look in the mirror and wonder how to get rid of my under-eye circles.

I have my periods of time where I'm 100% content, where I don't think about, worry about, or give any attention to my history of cancer. And then I'll have days that come at me hot with crippling anxiety.

In so many ways, I know who I am, more than I ever did in my *before*. To quote the always insightful Popeye, *I yam what I yam.*

In others, *I'm just not there yet.* I'm still *happening.* I'm still *unfolding.* I am still doing the Adam Brehm mantra: Listening. Learning. And trying to get better.

Life is constantly changing and so are we. Whether our years are numbered 84 or 22, we have a lot to figure out about this world and this life. We have endless capacity for growth. And if we all feel like *we're not there yet*, I think it's because we are, as a former boss often used to remind me, exactly where we are meant to be.

I'm not quite as mature as my ovaries. I'm not quite as young as my second batch of hair. I'm somewhere in the middle of my life—hopefully. I much prefer that to being at the end of things. So I think I'll just keep keepin' on and thanking the Big Guy Upstairs for all of these bonus days that I'm getting to experience goodness, get through the hard, and continue to soak up the sun (though yes, I'll wear sunscreen).

LESSON:

Celebrate the Normal Shit

Have you ever heard of Dr. Oz? No. Not the guy who is powering the voice from behind the curtain when Dorothy and her friends arrive from the yellow brick road, but rather the doctor guy who was always on the Oprah Winfrey Show talking about eating green vegetables. Do you know who I'm talking about?

If you do, perhaps you will understand why every time I think of Dr. Oz, I think of poop. And not because he was the shit. But because Dr. Oz was the guy who, via Oprah, educated me on the goal of the S Poop. I doubt that's the technical name for it. But it's the poop that you are supposed to work towards.

Yes, the poop. Stay with me here, okay.

I feel like poop is one of those things that all sorts of people get their underwear all bunched up over and yet, we *allllll* do it. Right? I MEAN, RIGHT? While I was never a stellar science student, I do believe that even if not by way of our bum, each and every human who takes in sustenance and liquids also has to excrete it. So, poop. As the book so beautifully sums it up: *Everybody Poops*. And yet it's sorta weird to talk about.

But Dr. Oz did a great thing. He told people, on a very popular platform, about ways to be able to tell if they are healthy. One, take a look at your pee. Check the color. If it's funky or too yellow, drink some more water. Two, get to know your poop.

Now, I am currently 36-years-old. That means that I have pooped a fair amount of times. That means that I have looked at my poop. And it means that when Dr. Oz told everyone that the secret to their health was in the appearance of their bowel movements, I found it fascinating.

What Dr. Oz said was that if you are eating the right foods then you should be both regularly dropping a deuce and that your turds should be one long snake-like poo. Yes. A turd that exits in one-fell-swoop, isn't tough to get out, and happens like clockwork.

So, I started striving for the S. Not straining though...that would have been against the goal. And I am proud to say that after some time of paying attention to my veggies and fruits, my water intake and the like, I, Ashli Brehm, became a regular S Pooper.

I get that Dr. Oz may have made that all up and his advice could be total shit. But I can say that feeling healthy, well, that for me felt like a win. I was (probably overly) happy to have *normal poop*.

Then I got pregnant and I can tell you that when, for the first time in my life, I experienced constipation, I was horrified. Here I was, a twenty-something gal who had only recently begun to acknowledge that I pooped and I found myself in torrential pain upon the throne. I longed for the S Poop to come back. I just wanted the normal shit.

Throughout pregnancy, I got everything back to its regular routine, only to eventually birth the child. The outcome of birthing the child was amazing. The fear that I felt as I needed to attempt to push out the first poop post-partum? That was completely awful.

Slowly but surely, the normal poop returned. I don't know if it was always the S Poop. It probably wasn't, but I didn't care given the fact that I had a human attached to my nipples and rarely had much time to visit the commode. With each new child, the same moment came a couple of days after delivery when I realized that once again, I was going to have to present a present for the hospital staff before they'd allow us to head home.

The poop. It's one of those things that we take for granted, that we do every day, that we don't really talk about, until it becomes a total pain in the ass.

When I began my first round of chemo, I was warned of the possible side effects. I signed a sheet that basically said I could be driven over by a car at some point and I had to be cool with that. The side effects included everything from hair loss to diarrhea to constipation to nerve damage to belching the ABCs backwards every time you farted (okay, not entirely true). But the possibilities that belie you when you are shooting toxic killing juice into your body are endless. But for me, the intended outcome outweighed any of the potential harsh effects.

I had excellent options for pain tolerance. Excellent antiemetics (technical term for non-barf drugs). I had magic mouthwash to numb the sores in my mouth. Though the hair fell, it was a relatively painless result once I cue-balled it. But the diarrhea...ohhhhhh, bless. It was a scene. The minute I ate something, I ran to the bathroom. I knew where every bathroom was in every single establishment I entered. It was basically like I was potty training another kid. The poo problem continued.

It was brutal.

During a second hospitalization due to treatment, a resident walked into my room. He immediately opened the bathroom door, walked out, and inquired, "Ummmmm...did you just use this bathroom?"

"Yes, yes I did. I tell you what, those chemo meds have completely messed with my stomach."

"Hmmmm. I think we're going to send a stool sample down to rule out infection."

Ohhhhh goody goody gumdrops. Yes. Please. Young, sorta attractive, smart resident. I would love for you to collect a little bit of my feces and hopefully, without gagging, get it down to the lab. That would be delightful and my one shining moment.

The lab test results returned and sure as shit, I had contracted C Diff.

C Difficile, or C Diff, is an infection that occurs when the gut biome is overcome with bad bacteria and cannot produce its good flora and typical gut environment. It was likely caused by the amount of antibiotics I'd needed when my counts dropped dangerously low. All the good gut bacteria was under attack and this led to a major shitfest. Serious stool time. Difficultly holding onto calories that were crucial to staying strong throughout chemotherapy.

My oncologist referred me to an infectious disease doctor who threw all the heavy hitting C Diff meds at my gut but I wasn't healthy enough to rebound and thus, my tank would need to be refilled. Yes, in order to get back to S Poop status, I needed to put up with someone else's shit.

This brilliant infectious disease doctor laid out the facts. We'd tried the very best meds available. I'd tried probiotics and prebiotics. Bone broth and LOW FODMAP diets. But I was also trying to beef up and hold onto as much weight as I could and so I needed to be able to eat the nutrient-dense foods I'd been avoiding because of my bumrush. So, it was recommended that after I completed chemo and surgery, I undergo a fecal transplant.

YES.

FECAL (feces, poop)

TRANSPLANT (to move from one thing to another)

She very appropriately and with a straight face, explained that the process of a fecal transplant would entail collecting donor feces and putting them into my gut. This process has shown great efficacy in re-growing the good gut flora (bacteria) and taking over the bad guys who are causing all of the poop calamities.

WHY DIDN'T I CELEBRATE THE NORMAL SHIT EVEN MORE WHEN I HAD IT?! WHY HAD I TAKEN MY S POOP FOR GRANT- ED?!

This is where I must say once again, *everyone poops*. And thank God that's the case. Because this girl needed a donor.

While I don't wish it on you or your dad or your cousin Larry, I must tell you that someday, you may need a fecal transplant. And your person who said *I do* may be your very best candidate to say "I poo," because you and yours share similar flora from living together and eating similar foods. So my husband produced a sample and, sweet mother of pearl, his poop was a match for me.

Honestly, I was thrilled. I know my husband's bathroom sched- ule. I was guessing he was a pretty regular dude with pretty nor- mal poop. Really, that's all I needed in my life and in my stom- ach. I didn't need some golden poop or the most pristine poop or poop that smelled like roses. The idea of sexy was already out the window. I figured at the point where he pooped in the jar, he was saying, "Yes, I'll stick around."

We scheduled the first time my husband would ever enter my exit for a time when he wouldn't even be allowed in the room.

I prepped for a colonoscopy, he produced an orange-sized (think navel, not cutie) sample, and we headed into the hospital for my third time under anesthesia in six months. The lab took the sample and blended it into a smoothie. My doctors and nurses prepped me in the OR. Then, I drank it.

Just kidding. I didn't drink it. Instead, I was put under anesthesia and performed a colonoscopy using the hose to introduce his good gut bacteria to my bad biome. Upon waking, they chal- lenged me to hold onto his donation for as long as I could.

The diarrhea ceased.

I held onto my husband's poop proudly, and a week later, my gut began to heal. The C Diff tests since have all come back clean. I am now eternally full of Adam's shit. Thankfully.

For months and months, I was so thankful, every day, for the normal shit. I would even think of Dr. Oz and the S Poop and be so grateful that in having good poop, I could be reminded that I was in good health.

In life, after cancer, I was so thankful for the normalcy of so many things. Soaking in a bath after having dealt with drains. Sleeping on my stomach again after months of only sleeping on my back. Not having pains radiating from the inside of my bones. The blessings of an average life. The reality of having so many things go *right* every single day. Sometimes we think the everyday stuff is just minutia. Sometimes we take the way our bodies miraculously perform as a given. So many times, we think that the little victories aren't a big deal. But truly, I promise you, all the normal shit is always worth acknowledging.

A year after my first cancer-free-versary, I started a new drug to minimize my chance of recurrence. Again, my stomach took a beating. I knew where every toilet was once again and never went out in public without my running shoes in the event that I needed to run to make the toilet. I often recalled the advice of one of my very intelligent and very funny brothers-in-law, Chris, when he told his children and mine to *never trust a fart*. Somehow, I made it through another year of crazy shit by the grace of the Good Guy and some leftover diaper cream I had from the baby phase.

Once again, I've found my way back to normal, at least in the poop department. And again, I find myself so grateful that everything has come out okay.

No one really likes to talk about poop. A lot of people like to act like they're not dealing with their own shit. Or that, if they are, it definitely does not stink. Butt. Everyone poops. Everyone does it. The normal shit, that's worth shouting from the rooftops every day. And celebrating that once again, everything came out all right. Just please wash your hands first.

LESSON:

Sex Isn't Always Sexy

Ohhhhhh, sex. Such a taboo topic that we aren't supposed to really talk about openly because it's private. But seriously, it's also bizarre. Like, bizarrely good and pleasurable if it's going right. But bizarre.

A friend recently said to me, "Gosh, I can't help it. We're like teenagers." I giggled to myself a little because for me, as a teenager, it was *pretty much* heavy petting central. It's totally awkward to figure out how to make out over a gearshift in the middle of the front seat of a car.

At my bachelorette party, I remember being perplexed when my wedding party educated me to the fact that you have to "clean up" after you do the deed. Ummmmm, what?! I thought you had wild, crazy, all night sex and then got to just fall asleep. BAHAHAHAHAHAHAHAHAHAHA! Still makes me laugh.

Newlywed sex is the bomb, though. Even if you do have some housekeeping items to tend to with sex, that whole honeymoon phase situation is legit the real thing. It's fun. Exciting. Easy. Pleasurable. And spontaneous. It's the type of sex that is portrayed on movies and TV. The stuff that's easy to talk about, sort of. The stuff that doesn't really require any moving parts outside of the two doing the boning. It's the good stuff, new sex. And it's hard to imagine how that would ever change, right?

I remember the first time the huz and I got back to basics after our first baby. I was not really sure how my business was going to welcome his boner. I mean...this area that had previously been for pleasure had morphed into this person-delivery mechanism. I actually pushed a human head and body out of my lady parts. And now, I was supposed to want to put man parts into it. Sheeeeeeesh.

We waited a hot minute, for sure, to get back into the swing of things. I took the six-week instructions from my midwife to be law and wouldn't even entertain the idea of being touched below the neck for that duration of time. But once the bits were all-clear, I felt that for my marriage and for my husband, we should get back on the horse. I know. That's terrible to admit. But ladies, I will say it without guilt. The *getting back to business after baby* had nothing to do with me. I think I probably could have gone a year after delivering each of my boys without even thinking about wanting to do anything resembling what had created each of them. This has nothing to do with my husband. He's hot. I am totally into him. I actually enjoy having him totally *into* me. But man alive... when my boobs were milk cartons and I had a baby nuzzling into my chest for 18 hours a day, the last thing I wanted to do was have a grown man groping that region.

So the first foray into foreplay post-baby wellllll...it was a rip-off the Band-Aid moment. Gah. That sounds so awful. And don't go getting your panties in a wad. I was not forced into the boning post-babe. I led the charge. But I had to psych myself up at that six-week mark. It felt like as much as I was terrified of his penis impregnating me again at that time, or of it ripping my vagina from top to Timbuktu, I really wanted to be close to my husband in the way we had been before baby.

The first, and second, and sixteenth time, golly geeeeeee—it was freaking painful. Of all the things that people *do* talk about regarding motherhood right now, I feel like this is something that no one really feels like it's kosher or acceptable to discuss.

Here's the thing though. Sex is important in a marriage, I think. It's something that, if all is well, you are only doing with that one person. It's like a little secret language that you and your spouse get to have. It's an extremely vulnerable experience. If it's all rocking and rolling, it should be something that you *both* enjoy and like and want. It shouldn't feel like *another thing* that you hafta do. But sometimes it does.

After about six months of realizing that post-baby sex wasn't always supposed to feel like you were living on the edge of your business being blasted apart, I talked to my doctor.

"I just feel like it's gonna rip into smithereens..."

Guess what?! There's a cream for that, sister! There are lots of ways to get your Girl Friday all gussied up for the ball. Errrr, balls. That's why man created lube! Grease up that puppy good and juicy before you get your jive on. Set the mood. Have some wine. Relax. And, as ridiculously unromantic as it sounds, for a bit...schedule it. Before you get down to Sextown, put your intentions in writing, commit to it. Make getting done a done deal.

Sounds like a lot of work for something that's supposed to be natural, right? Sounds like taking all the romance out of the romp, right? But seriously, sometimes in order to feel the rhythm and the rhyme, you gotta make sure your body knows it's bobsled time.

So. We did it. Like Nike tells us to.

And it started to work again. Just like it had.

Then we had another babe. And then, a couple years later, another. We knew, each time, that it might take time. But eventually, we would get to know our new normal.

It was something that I didn't know before children: the life in the bedroom would revolve around the lives outside of the bedroom. I didn't understand how the amount of time I spent being pulled on, fed off of, snuggled with, spit up all over, unshowered, and in an exhausted fog, would make me not want to be touched one more time by the end of the day. I didn't know that while sex is

184

something designed to bring you closer, it can be something that leaves you far apart when you are not having it. A life without orgasm can create a vast chasm where you once felt so grounded in your understanding of one another.

But it was a good thing, ultimately.

To go through the ups and downs of lacking ups and downs between the sheets was like the perfect preparation for what cancer would bring with it into the bedroom.

Sex and chemo. Gosh. This mama never planned on that.

Sex and chemo, well, it's a wild ride, should you choose to accept it. First, in case you're concerned, I asked...the chemo will not poison your spouse's parts. That was my first question. "If we want to *ya know* (wink wink nod nod)...is that *safe* or will the toxicity make his penis fall off?" My team assured me, it would not. And to date, it has not. So that's positive.

My second issue: there was no water on the slip and slide. Being in chemo meant, for me, being in menopause. I had no lube in the tube. This made for harsh weather conditions. So much like post-babes. It was like the Sahara down south. And no amount of foreplay or fooling around was about to make the hoses turn on again.

So again, with the lube. Balm that babymaker up before you even think about letting anyone ride the slide. Then do it again, multiple times, in multiple ways, in order to grease the wheels. Just buy the economy-sized bottle, cool? Cool.

And the third thing: I was bald. My body was being eradicated of a disease through toxic drugs. And that whole idea of what society calls "sexy" had gotten off the bus about four stops ago.

But *I* wanted to be close to my huz. I wanted to speak that secret language. Some don't even want to think about it during treatment. Some women don't want to be touched their whole pregnancy. Some don't want to be pursued until their youngest is 12. All couples have different sexpectations. And that's okay. The approach that you and yours take in the bedroom should be *yours.* What isn't okay is feeling like it's just always about the dude. Or that it's just not gonna be enjoyable because of babies or chemo or stress or...or. Just throwing in the towel because you don't want to have to lay down a towel.

Treatment paved the way for post-mastectomy recovery. And post-mastectomy was similar to post-babies in the way that I didn't want to be touched or caressed. I wanted to heal before any sexual healing took place. I had drains attached to my breasts. Or rather, the shells that had once housed my breasts. I had hard, plastic expanders in place of breast tissue.

We worked through that. We worked through the reality that the nipples that sit upon my chest don't actually serve any purpose outside of marking the middle of my mounds as boobs instead of just general fat that might sit on the rest of a body. We worked through the healing after two more surgeries. The changes of boob size and position, three times over. The realities of how sex in menopause at age 36 is different than sex as a newlywed at age 24.

It's this whole weird part of life, sex is. Sex and growing up. Growing into different life experiences. And sometimes, losing your drive to do the ditty. It's this hugely personal part of a relationship that I think we all want to be good, but it's something that doesn't really get talked about. When it's good...oh gah...there's nothing better. But when it feels like work, it feels like you're doing something wrong even when you're not.

Sometimes even the good parts of life take work. Sometimes even the most personal stuff, someone needs to talk about so we know we're not alone. And sometimes, well, you're gonna just be walkin' through the desert, together.

I know everyone talks about "getting your sexy back," but it's not at all about *going back*. It's about happily finding your new normal by going forward. It's about taking where you are and not comparing it to where you were. And eventually figuring out that this place where you are now is actually good, too.

Sex and chemo. Sex in motherhood. Sex and babies. Sex in pregnancy. Sex in general. It might not always be sexy. It might take some work. It doesn't have to be hard. But it always helps if he is.

LESSON:

I Will Start and Stop and Start Over and Over Again

I started yoga-ing. Again.

If there were a book about my life (oh wait. That's what this is.) it would probably be named, *She Started. Over and Over Again.*

I have spent a lot of my life starting. I started writing this very book when Barrett was in preschool and I was pregnant with Jonah. I started again when Barrett was in kindergarten, Jonah was in preschool, and I was pregnant with Harrison. I started, yet another *again*, when Harrison was about 18-months-old. And again several times since cancer entered my life. I have spent a lot of time starting. Again.

So. Back to yoga.

I started practicing yoga (or as Harrison called it when he was 4, "Woga") when I was a newlywed. I loved it. The first class, I was a hot mess. Truly. That's not being generic or basic. It was, indeed, *hot* yoga. I was dripping like a Nebraskan in a Texas Summer. Probably because I was a Nebraskan in Texas.

It was a time in my life where, although things were good, they were also sort of terrifying. Not terrifying like guy-in-your-house-during-a-horror-movie terrifying but more like the terrifying feeling of trying on the wrong sized shirt in a dressing room and not being able to get it off and feeling so certain they are going to have to cut you out of it and you're going to have to pay for the damaged shirt that you can't wear because it's shredded in half. Not that I've ever been there. Just imagining that would add up to some version of terrifying.

Texas was an adjustment. I'd just recently graduated college, gotten married to this guy that I was super keen on, and then, after returning from our honeymoon, packed up a U-Haul and driven south for 14 hours. I was embarking on an adventure to a new state and place. Austin, Texas. A place that was vibrant and *cool.* A booming, growing tech community. A place that was vastly different than my home base of Wilber, Nebraska—the town I grew up in, the place I loved being from.

And though I was excited for the whole being-a-grown-up thing, I can also admit, I was terrified.

I was terrified in that first yoga class because I didn't know what I was doing. I didn't know where I was going. It didn't feel any sort of *flow* because I didn't know what was next. I was surrounded by strangers who seemed to know what they were doing, but I was beaded in sweat. Some of the poses stretched me in ways I didn't want to be stretched. They were unfamiliar to my muscles and my form. They were testing my patience and my limits. Thirty seconds of a pose felt like a lifetime of challenge.

And yet, eventually, the more I practiced, the more yoga became this comfortable place and thing for my world.

But it took time.

What a metaphor for life, right?

Sometimes we are both excited and terrified, like I was during that time. I had just gotten married. This was amazing. But also, whoa. This was heavy. Like, one day we were dating and then zippity zam zoom: "As long as we both shall live." We were navigating the 23rd and 25th years of our lives *together*. As *one*. But also as two very individual people.

It was unfamiliar. The beginning of the newness. Like the yoga studio, my surroundings in this new place felt like I was smack dab in the middle of the room, peering into a mirror and seeing myself surrounded...not alone...and I didn't know any of the people. They were simply like-minded people who all chose to be where I also chose to be in that moment.

I didn't know where I was going. I didn't have a job. I didn't know what my next pose was going to be. I felt so taken out of my comfort zone. I felt so stretched. I felt internally dripping in sweat. But on the outside, I was attempting to look like I had it all in order.

I was thrilled when a chance meeting at church got me an interview. That interview got me hired. My first real-world gig. Where, incidentally, I was a paid intern at a PR Agency. I was really bad at the job. Sure. At the time, I thought I had a handle on things. But then I found myself growing into an adult while trying to grow out of childhood and teenager-dom simultaneously. Trying to effectively play the part. Trying to get all the poses correct. Trying to pose firm on my mat. Trying to make it look effortless.

I struggled. Even though I met some of the best of the best, I still missed my people. Even though I was in a city with so much to do and so much to learn, I could not, for whatever reason, melt into the *mat*. I missed the ease of the poses I'd grown comfortable with. The place my muscles and my bones had become accustomed to.

And then I was told that something in my future might be hard. Having babies. It might be hard because of a health condition I'd dealt with for a few years. A person who didn't even really know me said, "This will be different than it is in the textbooks." And so, without much thought, I took that and ran with it. That warning was just enough to completely knock me off my balance. I rolled up my mat. We moved.

I started yoga again after Harrison was born. I was so scared, again, *to start*. I was so scared to go into a room of fancy people doing fancy things. Me, with my $13 Amazon Prime'd mat. Wearing my Big Box store active-wear. Next to the Lulu Gurus. I felt timid. But I knew what I *could* feel if I just started. Again.

And so I did it. I started yoga. Again. And I kept. on. going. For months on end I went and stretched into downward dog. I went and started to flow comfortably into pigeon pose. When the instructor said things like, "Utkatasana," I no longer thought it was someone sneezing. I began to let go when I got onto the mat. It began to feel like something that came naturally to me.

Then cancer. And chemo. I got sick. Really sick. As one does with treatment, I watched my white blood cell counts crash so much that I couldn't be around germs. Or in hot rooms with people who also harbored germs and coughs and sickies. And so I stopped. Again.

I was pissed this time. I wanted to be able to go into the yoga room and shut out my reality. But I was so crashed somedays that I could only walk, Adam and the boys beside me, to the stop sign and back. Yoga went to the wayside. The mat became a staple of decorating amidst the randomly-scattered coats and backpacks through the laundry room. I *did* cancer.

As I recovered, I wondered if I had the balls to do yoga again. (I knew, for certain, that I didn't have the boobs.) Could I work myself up to start again? Again?

I'd already started and stopped. Started and stopped. I didn't want to chance hurting my arm or my chest. I didn't want to know that I'd been able to feel comfort in that place and now, again, I would feel like the new girl in town.

But one day I just did it. I started again. I picked up my $13 mat after 18 months and started. Again.

It was hard. I had to relearn what my new body was ready for. I had to shut out what my favorite yoga teacher, Liz, called "the drunk monkey" that follows us through life. The mind chatter, which in yoga language is apparently called the chitta vritti. The little voice that exists in our mind and tells us that we *can't*. The chatter that takes our focus off the present and has us worried about the hour after class or the week ahead. I had to tell that little dude to evacuate my yoga mat.

The $13 mat was upgraded. My yoga teacher surprised me with a beautiful, brand-named mat that in my previous *starts* would have felt frivolous. Because what if I stopped again? Then I'd have this even more expensive reminder of my inability to push through.

But, on it, my balance was better. My ability to stand my ground was firmer. Somehow, I could feel the journey in the mat. I knew that there were going to be poses I couldn't do. I knew my arms and my binds would not come as easily then. If not ever. I knew it would take patience and time.

Just weeks after starting, once again I felt like I could breathe. I felt like I could let myself be who I was in that spot. It was good. Again. It was good.

But then another medication called Nerlynx dropped into my treatment plan. A whole ton of tummy troubles accompanied it. When diarrhea began to disrupt my downward dog, I stopped yoga. Yes. Again.

I knew by then that there are just going to be times in life when we have to stop or say no to something. It's not that we're saying *not ever*. It's merely a *not right now*. The things that we need to say *no* to for a time, but not for all time.

Sure enough, that year and the pooping passed. I got back to the mat. But this time, it didn't feel like a restart. It felt like part of the flow of life. Starting. Stopping. Starting again.

I stood in a class right after the New Year, the room packed mat-to-mat. I listened to the cues in Guided Flow. I told that little drunk monkey trying to chat me up to take a seat outside.

Without even knowing where I was going, I found myself in a pose that I hadn't even attempted since the *before*. I found my-self in a bind and yet I felt so damn free. I had forgotten that my mind thought I couldn't. I had forgotten that maybe my shoulder and my arm thought I shouldn't. I just went with the flow and let myself go.

It was another moment of healing. As we lay in Savasana, translated to "Corpse Pose," I didn't feel dead. My eyes filled with tears—yes, I even cry in yoga class—and I knew that life is a practice, always in motion. That the stopping, starting, stopping, starting…it's okay to do over and over again…from birth to earth.

LESSON:

My Dreams Are Never Too Big

*I*n September of 2008, I decided to start my blog. Was this because I was a writer by trade? No. Was it because I was independently wealthy and a lady of leisure who needed a hobby? Nope. Was it because I had studied up and researched "blogs" and determined that it was my very own route to fame, wealth, and lifelong recognition? Nuh-uh. Not that either.

I just wanted to start a blog.

I came up with the name without much deliberation: Baby on the Brehm. To me, it was clearly spot on. Our last name *Brehm*, said BRAME, would make for a perfect double entendre to the blog's moniker. I was pregnant with our first child. The baby was *on* me, *the Brame*. And also, said quickly, it sounded like Baby on the Brain. *YES! Witty! Funny! Perfection.*

But notsomuch when everyone thinks your last name is pronounced *Bremm.*

Nevertheless, I persisted. And Baby on the Bremm or Brame had staying power in my life.

I blogged about feeling as if a baby was really just an alien burrowing about in my stomach, trying to break free like that weird
scene in Space Balls where the little animal busts out of some
guy's belly. I blogged about my journey on bed-rest and how my
adjustment to motherhood was not as seamless as I'd imagined
it would be. Each time we found out we were pregnant, I shared
all of the happenings of each of my boys from their very beginnings. I blogged about pushing a baby out of my vagina and
having one cut out of my stomach. When we lost a pregnancy,
I shared the sadness and grieving I experienced. When, after
having already experienced bringing premies into the world two
times over, we welcomed our third at 32 weeks, I shared about
our adventures in the NICU.

In 2015, when the boys who were the impetus for the blog were
6, 4, and 2, I had my sort of Robert Frost moment. When the
beyond of my tagline became far more *real* and terrifying than I
ever imagined, I paused. I talked to God and my husband and I
questioned: *Do I keep writing?* I had come to a fork in the road
and I decided that I would do this whole *breast cancer thing* and
continue with my blog, chronicling all the moments. It would
serve as a way that I could share, in one central location, the
details of my treatment and prognosis. A way that I could take
the hard stuff and do what I'd been doing for all of my years of
motherhood...I would write in order to process the feelings. I
would write to be able to look back when we reached the *after* of
moving this mountain that had landed smack-dab in the middle
of my roadmap.

I will write, I secretly held to my heart, *in case I don't get to be
here because of this cancer. So my boys know that I tried. So
they never ever for one moment question if I loved them to the
moon and stars and beyond.*

And so, 25 days after I felt a lump, I clicked *post* on my new reality. I'd just begun *the hardest chapter to write.*

My blog following grew. It's not like I'm Beyoncé or the Queen
of England. But it did somehow grew to thousands following me
via social media. I received a phone call from a then stranger,

now close friend, Jenny, who worked for Nebraska Medicine, my treatment center, asking if I'd be up for them tagging along on my *journey* and adventures.

I prayed, once again, and talked with Adam. I feared that people might start trolling me or telling me stories of other young women who'd lost their battles with breast cancer. But I decided that if I could do any good in this situation, maybe I could share that even when life felt really hard, there could also still be so much good...when the skies felt dark, you could still look for the stars...when the going got tough, the tough didn't always get going...if I could share that point of view, the only point of view I knew how to have as a 33-year-old mother of three little boys, then *yes*. I would willingly invite people into my cancer chapter. And I would do it with every bit of authenticity that I possessed.

At some point, things started getting surreal. Not like Publisher's Clearing House showing up on my doorstep with balloons surreal. But more like Ashton Kutcher's Punk'd surreal.

I got a call from The Ellen Show. I was halfway through my six rounds of chemo. Someone left me a voicemail saying they were with The Ellen Show. I was immediately armed with the best comeback when I returned the call. "Hey, Ashli! This is Ian with the Ellen Show," he said.

"Uh huh. Yep! And I'm the Queen of England," I replied. "Did Debra and Diana tell you to do this?" I was in the middle of my kitchen in middle America and I was certain that a couple of my sorority sisters were pulling one of our old-fashioned prank phone calls.

"No. This is Ian. With the Ellen Show." Oh fluffermuffins. He wasn't kidding. And I'd just been completely ridiculous.

"Oh sheesh. I'm sorry..." The call proceeded. He asked me what famous people I loved and I said, "Ellen!" He asked me some other questions. I think he even asked me again what celebrities I love and I was so whacked out on chemo that I said something resembling, "I don't know. I just like normal people." When I finally got off the phone, I nearly shat myself.

Because first of all, it was The Ellen Show. I wasn't to tell a soul and, as per directed, I didn't until a very long time after. And second, *I just like normal people.* Okay. While I do adore all of my "normal" life people, I think the Ellen Show was looking for some kind of celebrity I love or some sort of dream I had. But instead, I said, *"I just really like normal people."* I mean, who freaking says that? Am I that altruistic? No. Was I that confused by the fact that I'd been called by The Ellen Show? Um, hell to the yes.

Nothing ever came of that call. I eventually had another call with a lovely gal from The Ellen Show. And while nothing came of that either, at least I didn't smack-talk that person. Then more craziness happened and throughout my cancer chapter, I also got to talk with some people from Inside Edition and GMA online when my plea on my Baby on the Brehm's Facebook Page for a bit of breast milk for my friend and fellow breast cancer survivor, Jackie, led to over 20,000 ounces being offered. When hundreds of people sent paper flowers and gifts for an 11-year-old Ewing's Sarcoma patient, Daisy, The Washington Post called. I somehow even got a tiny one-line quote about lube during menopause in an issue of Oprah Magazine.

None of these calls or conversations were life-altering. But the fact that it was a way for the true goodness of people to shine through some of the bullshit, well, that was soul-changing for me.

This choice to have shared my life, step by step as I slogged through the suck of cancer, ended up being one that I've never regretted. I have referred to the call I got from Jenny and the friendship we now have as things that have changed my life and my belief in goodness. I've gotten to see the best things happen to really good people, I've gotten to be inspired by a whole community of souls who believe there is goodness to be felt and found, and I've even gotten to be a part of so many things that are far beyond what I could have ever been a part of on my own. I've gotten to see and know goodness and the power of people to spread it. It's the best part of it all.

I didn't start blogging to become an *influencer* or to make millions from *clicks*. I get that that's a legitimate profession in the current arena, but it wasn't even in my imagination when I signed on to tell my story. I didn't start blogging to be a therapist or an expert. I started blogging to be a storyteller. And from day one, that is what I've gotten to do.

So I decided to write this book. To tell my story. Three years ago, right after cancer was complete, I told myself I'd start on my next adventure. Compiling all these lessons into one central place where I could locate them if the wind started whipping my sails.

In the book's infancy, I basically figured I'd just run it through a ditto machine and present copies to my family and close friends, pages still damp and blotted with bluish purple ink, perhaps three-hole punched and tied with ribbon. But as I began to write and talk about it, the idea grew. Eventually, I found myself wandering into the wild west world of traditional publishing.

A friend was kind enough to supply me with a woman I could talk with. A woman who had been legit successful in the publishing industry. A woman who had seen the writing scene and lived to work in it. And this woman was willing to take my call. She was willing to let me pick her brain.

It was in that phone call that I learned something about myself. **I am not famous enough to be famous**.

To be fair to her, I suppose I didn't really *learn* that from her. I already knew that. In fact, when the voice on the other side of the phone—the one who sat in New York City as I sat on the floor in my home in Omaha—relayed to me why I ought not pursue a literary agent, she wasn't telling me anything that was shocking to 36-year-old-no-longer-housing-cancer *me*. **You're not famous enough to be famous**. She stated it so evenly. "Oh. Yeah. I know I'm not famous. I guess I wasn't trying to be famous." I think I might have even laughed a bit as I responded to her. I think I'd wondered if she'd confused me with her call with the celebrity chef she had calendared for later that day. I just wanted to have a book published. *Was I supposed to want to get famous from it?*

198

She continued on with her assessment of my lack of stardom, our conversation going something like: "Everyone wants to be a writer. I mean, you have some skill. And you are even kind of funny. But you definitely don't write the kind of writing I enjoy reading. The people who get agents and get published? Those people are people who are going to make money for the publisher."

And *pause*. I just sat for a moment on the other end of her words. I realized I'd been holding my breath and upon my exhale, I told her I appreciated her candor. After all, I was just going to ditto the book in the first place. Clearly I'd gotten drunk at some point and believed I was worth being read. Clearly I forgot that I was *just a gal from Nebraska*. I told her that I appreciated her time. And that was that.

How silly had I been that I *thought* I could actually publish a book? How ridiculous that I even let myself get past the idea of printing a book at Kinkos and calling it good? How dumb that I'd let my hopes raise to the idea that I might have a story to share.

I cried as I relayed the story to my husband. I wasn't crying because my dreams had been crushed. After all, it wasn't my dream to publish with a publisher in the first place. I cried because I felt like my dreams had been minimized. I felt like I had been told that because I was not of great importance to people in a big office in the city, I might as well take my ball and go home. And stay there.

Adam, of course, told me the woman was dumb because my husband is the Prez of my Fan Club. While I definitely don't think she was dumb, I do think he was able to help me remember that she was not my audience.

Then I remembered something that Barrett, my Oldest, had told me. In fact, he'd drawn it on a picture that was framed on the wall of my office. The room I sat in at that moment, feeling like a big pile of *stupiddreams*.

I looked at the white frame and read: **Your dreams are never to big**.

Gah. What is it about kids that they *get it* so often when we are being stupid? The poster (grammatical errors aside) was exactly on point. Your dreams are never to big.

Also. They are never too big.

If we need to get technical.

He was eight. I was 36. And he was just the goodness I'd needed in that moment.

The woman was right. The woman on the phone told me, **you're not famous enough to be famous**. And she was right, because I wasn't. But she also didn't know me. She didn't know my dream had nothing to do with being famous. My dream was simply to complete the task of writing a book, share my moments and lessons from *my* time with cancer and provide a little bit of goodness and *hope* for whomever had their eyes on the words.

I forgot as she spoke that what she was telling me was my greatest pitfall was also never my intention in the first place. I'd started this blog in 2008. I'd kept writing because it gave me joy and contentment. I'd written about cancer to help in my healing. I'd learned that I could share goodness. I believed that there might be one or two people out there who might find hope in that goodness.

My dream was not too big. She just wasn't the right person to give it gusto. I knew that going into the call. I knew I was not the type of writer she represents. I had known going in that she wasn't going to publish me. But I forgot it somewhere in-between the beginning and the feedback she provided.

Thank God for my 8-year-old. Thank God he knew a thing or two about dreaming.

It was a phone call I will never forget. Similar to the ones from people at TV shows and reporters for magazines. A call where I was reminded that while I might be *just a girl from Nebraska,* that has no impact on my capacity to dream. Or my right to dream big. And even more importantly, as my therapist, Barb, reminds me so often, "What someone else thinks of me is none of my business." While I think that is also something from Alcoholics Anonymous, I think all of us—whether we drink or have never touched the stuff—are well-served to remember that the way others interpret our actions does not define the intent.

I decided that shopping this book for traditional publishing was not the direction I would go. I decided I'd write the book I wanted to. And that my dream to do so was just right.

We are here for a moment in time. We might as well try with all of our might to make something of it. Maybe it is your dream to be famous. That's awesome. Stick with that dream. Maybe it is your dream to get out of bed every day and find the magic in that. Maybe your dreams land somewhere in-between and are always changing. But. Whether your dreams make sense to someone else or not, always remember this: *even if you're not famous enough to be famous, your dreams, my dear, are never to big.*

LESSON:

I Could Have Missed This

I think it often when I lay my head down on my pillow at night. About what a day we had.

About all the mini moments that had me laughing. The times where I held a hand of a little human who looked to me with adoring eyes. The times where a heavy eye roll was a response from a child as I oh-so-patiently (ahem) reminded him to be kind. About the times where fits were thrown. The moments where I lost my cool. Or when I didn't lose my cool. The way it felt to sit and eat dinner and be thankful together. The moments where I sat and looked at the sun shining outside in my backyard and realized what a ridiculously cool thing it is...to be alive in a time such as this.

I think through what was good about the day. What was hard. What seemed to work. What didn't. What I got done. What is yet to do. Or to be done.

And nearly every day at some point I think, "I could have missed all this." One thing could have gone different at any one point and my life would be a different story.

I could have missed all this.

I could have missed my boys experiencing ages 8, 6, and 3. Or 10, 7, and 5.

I could have missed late evenings laughing with people who I count among the best of the very best.

I could have missed the moments catching up with family from near and far and realizing what a quilt our lives are...patch by patch, connected by similar threads.

I could have missed the joy of a fresh, hot cup of coffee in the morning.

I could have missed the feeling of fullness when I lay my head on my husband's chest at the end of every day.

I could have missed the beauty of a new show becoming available on Netflix and being able to watch it, whenever the heck I want.

I could have missed the way it feels to sleep on clean sheets.

I could have missed the way my boys love to read and draw and play...all with each other.

I could have missed hearing the Littlest's squeaky squawky talk.

I could have missed the Middlest learning how to deal when stuff doesn't go his way.

I could have missed the Oldest being so old.

I could have missed it all. But I didn't have to.

...

I lay down next to my Littles each night and hum their bedtime tune. I rub their backs. I think not about all that has gone wrong in the day, but rather all that has gone right in order for us to be in this moment, lying together side by side.

I hear their breathing slow. Their heavy sighs as they fall into dreamland. I even take a mental picture of their long eyelashes melted under their eyes. I do. Because it's the little beautiful pieces that stick in my mind at night. I kiss them each on the head and say, "Good night, sweet boy. Mommy and Daddy love you."

...

I could have missed all of this. Any one of us could. But we are where we are for a reason, I believe.

I don't know all the reasons or ways that life is hard. But I know that the goodness, for me, has made even the hardest parts survivable.

Things could have easily gone very differently. But for me, they didn't. And so I find myself thankful for the reminder that when the night falls, I lived another day.

And what a crazy thing that is.

Every single time.

LESSON:

It Is the Ordinary That Makes This Extraordinary

We get time. As I say, over and over, life takes *time*, if we're lucky. So even though we are all dying, we don't say that, do we? We don't say it until we're sick. Or scared. Or somehow losing the ability to live.

It's called life because it's meant to be life-full. It's meant to be lived.

And not be dying.

We are not to wait until we are dying to do life. We are to live it in each day.

We are to find the things that bring us joy—our career, our family, our God, our children, our fur-kids, experiences, activities—and do them. Not wait for them.

I'm now 37. I hopefully have a ton of years ahead of me. But seriously, no one knows for sure.

My approach as it stands today is to continue to live. To remind myself that every day of my life, the sun has set, and in the morning that has followed, the sun has risen. And so, my biggest goal is to live.

Living has made me want to do all the cliché things that are supposed to make me feel alive.

On my first cancer-free-versary, a year after the day I got the call that my pathology was clear, I jumped from a plane. I was almost 35. I'd survived cancer. My husband kissed me and wished me good luck before I went up in a plane and dropped out overlooking the Florida coastline.

I trained for and completed a half marathon. Seriously, I hate running. Usually I would say that you shouldn't do things you hate because you don't need to invite negativity into your world. But in doing the half, I got to experience standing with my dad, my brother, and Adam at the finish line, and it felt like I'd told cancer to suck it.

I sang, on my second cancer-free-versary. My friend, Jenny, agreed to my crazy idea for me to sing and strum my guitar on the main floor of the Buffett Cancer Center, the home-base for my care team.

And for my third cancer-free-versary? Well, you're reading that big scary dream of mine right now.

We're making family goals, like visiting every state in the US. And to travel anywhere else we can. We want to experience the world with our boys, but we also want them to know that just like their home state, even the states known as "flyover states" have good people, good food, and good lessons for life.

Those are some of the bigger *bucket* items. But most days... most days we are soaking up the **normal.**

We spend holidays with family, playing cards, watching movies, playing football, and enjoying the water. Almost every time, I cry at some point because I'm so thankful for the time.

206

We spend evenings with friends. Couples who have become like family to us. We eat delicious meals and play ridiculous games.

I laugh until my belly hurts on nights out with girlfriends. Talking about kids, marriage, sex, and being women. Sharing a bottle of wine and shutting the restaurant down.

Each night that we sit at the dinner table, we share Thankfuls before we eat and then, holding hands, we sing the Johnny Appleseed Song (Yes, this is true. No, we aren't the Partridge Family. We sang the Johnny Appleseed when I was growing up and Thankfuls was a thing we added when the boys were little). And of course, one of our boys drives me bananas by complaining about the food. I mean, we're still an ordinary family.

Every morning I wake and I look at my bedside table. I glance quickly. It is in my eyesight and I can't dodge it even if I wanted. I see the note I wrote to myself on the day that I got the call that my cancer was gone. A sticky note with the logo for The Fred and Pamela Buffett Cancer Center is framed. The frame sits on my nightstand, my handwriting scrawled on the note reminding me: Today I am not sick. Today I am grateful for God. And my family. And my medical team. And my friends. And goodness. Every day.

That sticky note reminds me of people like Pamela, who have endured hardships and kept on keeping on, spreading goodness. It reminds me of my friend, Leslie, who believes that anything written on a sticky note can come true. It reminds me that every day is a new day. And that there will be goodness, even if the day starts with my two youngers screaming in their room, the news headlines being all sorts of Negative Norman, or the coffee maker being on the fritz.

Because badness will be here. Imperfection will be ever-present. Problems will occur. Lumps may pop up. And even coffee is not a given.

Life, for the most part, is unpredictable and ever-changing.

My kitchen counter is not always spotless. There is often pee on the wall of any bathroom you enter in my house. My boys are not dressed to the nines but rather prefer athletic wear 24/7/365. Sometimes I completely lose my crap on my boys. Sometimes, it's for good reason. Sometimes, it's not. Some days the last thing I'm interested in is canoodling with my husband. Once the boys are in bed for the night, I sometimes fall into mine, exhausted from nothing out of the ordinary having occurred. I have lazy days. And the first time in a decade of blogging, I will go weeks without typing up anything new.

But.

Life feels full.

Because I'm wearin' the swimsuit.

Wearing the damn swimsuit does not mean that every time the sun rises I hop out of bed and light the world on fire. It means that the lessons I've taken from cancer and life are imprinted on my heart and that every day the sun comes up is another chance to give it all a whirl. And every new day reminds me that just because I didn't get it all done yesterday doesn't mean I can't today. And whether I'm 37, 66, or 82, I am reminded that I'm never too old to start something new. Or stop and take a breather. I don't need to give fear the power to freeze me... if I really want to experience something or keep unfolding, I can let the fear fuel me to a point of putting on the swimsuit and lighting this world right up. Ultimately, every day I'm here is my extra time to make this the best day I've never yet lived.

After cancer, I am much less likely to say *yes* to something just because I feel like I should. I am much less likely to feel like my thighs nuzzling one another or my stomach looking like Jabba the Hut when I look back at it in Downward Dog is cause for a quick *fix*. I am less likely to forget to say *I love you*. And I am more likely to eat dessert, have a glass of wine, or tell someone about my poop (clearly).

This life I live is not fancy or worthy of fame. But it is mine. And that's what I like most about it. Not every day brings travels or adventures. In fact, most of my days are very ordinary, and yet each and every one of them now feels extra to me.

After all, every second we get is one more than we are guaranteed. So whether I'm skydiving, doing laundry, or watching the boys throw down, somehow, through cancer and life, even the most normally abnormal moments can feel pretty extraordinary.

Let the hard stuff be hard. Feel the goodness when it's good. And if it just feels dark, you can always take the opportunity to shine your light. Have fun. Live live the crap out of life when you can. And of course, whatever your is, *wear the damn swimsuit.*

ACKNOWLEDGEMENTS...

To be completely transparent, *acknowledgements* make me have sweaty pits because I worry about forgetting someone or making someone feel like crap because I don't mention them. But. I'm going to do it anyway because *wear the damn swimsuit*, right?

I would call this my Oscar speech but really, the music would kick me off stage after my first paragraph.

I've been writing at BabyontheBrehm for ten years: to those who have been reading since the beginnings of my Blogspot address, those who have come in the middle, or those who have read a post here and there -- thank you for following my blog, for giving my words wings, and for giving me the gift of getting to be myself. You are true goodness.

To the family I was born with—Mom, Dad, Matthew, and Danielle—thank you for *always* loving me for the crazy person I am. I will forever hold memories of cheese fries, family campouts, and the Johnny Appleseed song in my heart and believe that because of the four of you, I grew up knowing what love is. Being attached to all of you might be my greatest accomplishment. I am so proud to have grown up an Eickman.

To my aunts, uncles, and cousins, thank you for being true to the meaning of family. The roots of the tree are what allow it to grow tall and spread its branches. Everyone should be so lucky to have such *rich* soil as a foundation for life.

To the family I've gained through love and vows—Laura, Chris, and the Brehms—thank you for letting my story be part of yours.

Laura and Chris, I love that we can make a game with Squigz, make fun of Steak O Poyver, and all agree that every day is a good day for happy hour. I love how I can't imagine the Eickman family without you.

To the Brehm bunch. Lyle and Kathy, I had no clue when I met you that I'd love you like I do. Thank you for caring for me like one of your own. Kevin, Lynn, Eric, Emilie, and Kim – I love getting to be a Brehm with you. I love playing Liar's Dice and eating biscuits and gravy. I love how you've made me a person who loves the lake and the word *lollygag*. I am proud to get to share your last name.

To my 11 nephews and 2 nieces, I will gladly own the title of your craziest relative as long as you will always be the awesome people you are. You have brought a joy to my life that is different than any other. I am so proud of your parents for raising such cool, kind, respectful, cute, smart people. I hope you will never get *too old* or *too cool* to hang with me.

To my life-earned *framily* including but not limited to – Andersons, Petersons, Wilbers, Libby, Anuj, Sapna, Doug, Judi, Shane, and Logan -- the fact that you've chosen to allow me to know you and be loved by you is pretty wonderful. From Holidays to Crashli Duty and everything in-between, you've been our *people* right alongside our family. You completely kick ass. Thanks for doing that.

To our besties -- women and couples we celebrate with, we travel with, eat dinner with, have drinks with, and laugh with over and over again -- thank you for showing me that true friendship is the best thing money can't buy. The Ashli's Angels' Tribe – Betsy, D, Debra, Diana, Julie, Kacie, Karin, Kayla, Kristin, Missy, Nicole – I love you. And to the husbands, you are some of the best of the best.

To alllll the women who taught me that women need women, whether I met you in Wilber, through Phi Mu, in Austin, at work, across the street, at school, in Bible Study, at church, or in other parts of life, I feel fortunate to have you in my corner. Thank you Nicky, Sara, Sarah, Shannon, and others for Marco Poloing with me as a daily reminder that friends are the goodness of life. Thanks to all of my peeps who put up with my lack of answering text messages. Thank you for being people who I am better because of.

To all those from our 'hood, schools, church, and community, who swooped in and cared for my kids like your own, prayed for us, showed up, and who continue to show me that we are all one village, thank you for being such a community of badass females. To those who I've met through cancer, I hate that it's what connects us but I love that I get to know you. And to Emily and Cass, thanks for coming over weekly through treatment and making our house feel more like home.

To Dr. Saxena, thank you for saving my life by simply following your gut and ordering a mammogram. You are an incredible doctor and family friend.

To my extensive care team at Nebraska Medicine and Village Pointe Aesthetics as well as some advisers from Southeast Nebraska Cancer Center, thank you for being compassionate, curious, and cure-seeking. Dr. Johnson, Dr. Tandra, Dr. Thayer, Dr. Wahl, Deb, Judeen, Lisa, Meg, and Stacey, you have been a dream team for me. Catherine, Dr. Green, and Dr. Peterson, thank you for being my adviser team from Southeast Nebraska Cancer Center. To Dr. Freifeld, Amanda, and Dr. Hewlitt, thank you for helping me get my poop in a group. To Barb Clinkenbeard, thank you for helping through the *unfolding* and in my life *beyond*.

To all "my" incredibly caring, joyful, and hope-providing nurses at the Village Pointe clinic, Infusion Center, and Village Pointe Aesthetics -- *I love you people*. Amber, Bailey, Betty, Carissa, Debbie, Denise, Emily, Gabriella, Jaci, Joanna, Johanna, Julie, Katie, Katy, Lindsey, Megan, Michelle, Sarah, Stacey, Sue, Teresa, Toni... each of you made an impact in my treatment. Dawn, Genie, Jen, Lori, Ruth, Traci... thank you for all the scheduling and communicating you did and continue to do for appointments, labs, and shots. Jeff and Tom, thanks for being two of my favorite drug dealers. Glenda, thank you for rocking the Wig Bank. Jenny Nowatzke you are brilliantly talented and wonderfully kind. And to all the marketing peeps, thank you for allowing me to chronicle my journey with Nebraska Medicine and UNMC.

To Pamela, thank you for asking a stranger to lunch and reminding me that we all have our story to tell. To both you and Peter, the Foreword is so far beyond what I ever could have imagined it would be. Thank you for all of your time and kindness. To Cindy and Kristin, may we always have time for our annual ladies' lunch.

To Leslie, thank you for talking me through being someone who has words to someone who will call herself a writer. And to all the Her View From Home writers, you rock. It's a great thing when women support women.

To those who have hired me to speak, write, and allow me to be a storyteller, thank you for helping me pursue my passion. To the businesses who have contributed to my Giftaways, you rock. And to Daisy, and Jackie, thank you for letting me be a part of goodness in action.

To alllllll who helped this dream of mine, this book, come together, you da best. Specifically Jan, and Rachel Carter with Yellowbird Editors, thank you for your wisdom and talent. And to all who read excerpts and helped this come together, I have so much gratitude for you.

To EVERYONE – the Army, the Angels, the businesses, non-profits, and the strangers -- who *did what they knew how to do* for my family and for me I will never be able to pay you back but I will forever try to pay it forward.

I am thankful for a God who has loved me from before I even began and has put me on the earth with so many wonderful humans.

I told you this list would be long. Brevity has never been a strength of mine. And gratitude is my jam.

Lastly, big time love and snuggles to my Barrett, Jonah, Harrison, and my Adam. You have given me more lessons and life than I feel worthy of. In writing every bit of this book, I did it so I can always tell you to take chances, tell your story, and be who you are. No matter what, I will love each of you more than any words will ever be able to communicate. I only hope that you will never forget that more than anything, I want you to *wear the damn swimsuit.*

Always and forever, Go Big Red.

Ashli

To read more of Ashli's musings on
motherhood, cancer, and life, visit

www.babyonthebrehm.com

 @babyonthebrehm

For information on booking Ashli to speak, email
babyonthebrehm@gmail.com

35126216R00124

Made in the USA
San Bernardino, CA
07 May 2019